LAVOISIER—THE CRUCIAL YEAR:

The Background and Origin of His

First Experiments on Combustion in 1772

Antoine Laurent Lavoisier, 1743–1794, a portrait
by David   (Photo Roger-Viollet)

LAVOISIER – *The Crucial Year*

The Background and Origin of His

First Experiments on Combustion in 1772

By *Henry Guerlac*

CORNELL UNIVERSITY

CORNELL UNIVERSITY PRESS

Ithaca, New York

This work has been brought to publication with
the assistance of a grant from the Ford Foundation.

CORNELL UNIVERSITY PRESS

First published 1961

Library of Congress Catalog Card Number: 61-14953

PRINTED IN THE UNITED STATES OF AMERICA

BY VAIL-BALLOU PRESS, INC.

TO

Andrew Norman Meldrum

(1876–1934)

AND

Hélène Metzger

(1889–1944)

Acknowledgments

MUCH of the research and much of the writing of a first draft of this book was completed while I was a member of the Institute for Advanced Study, Princeton, in 1953–1955. To the Institute's distinguished director, Dr. J. Robert Oppenheimer, and to the late Edward Mead Earle, I am especially indebted for the privilege of those two unhampered years of research and study. I wish to thank Mrs. Marian Hartz for secretarial assistance and Miss Judith Sachs, librarian of the Institute, for guiding an importunate visitor to needed reference materials and to the riches of the great Rosenwald collection of rare books in the history of science.

The completion of the manuscript was postponed until I could consult the second volume (1957) of Lavoisier's *Correspondance*, covering the years 1772–1775. In the meantime, with the resources of Cornell's fine basic collection in the history of science, I was able to dispose of certain controverted matters—such as the dating of Lavoisier's February memorandum—and publish the results separately as articles. At all stages of my investigations I have drawn extravagantly on my treasury of grace with the devoted staff of the Cornell University Library. I owe special thanks to Dr. Felix Reichmann for his speed and skill in obtaining rare books for the collection and to Miss Josephine Tharpe and Miss Frances Lauman for the many services reference librarians in their mysterious way know how to perform. I wish also to thank their colleagues in the other American libraries where I have worked, especially the Harvard University Library, the Princeton University Library, and the libraries of the New York Academy of Medicine and of the American Philosophical Society in Philadelphia. For their willingness to send rare books and periodicals on interlibrary loan, I am grateful to a number of institutions and persons, especially to the Yale Medical Historical Library under the direction of Dr. Frederick Kilgour and to the University of Wisconsin, which has generously made available rare items from its remarkable collection of works in early chemistry.

Like many another foreign scholar, in Paris I have enjoyed the hospitality of the Bibliothèque Nationale, the library of the Institut de France and of the Muséum d'Histoire Naturelle. At the archives of the Académie des Sciences I have been helped on repeated occasions by Mme Pierre Gauja and her staff with that unfailing courtesy and efficiency they have shown so many visiting historians of science.

Aid and stimulation have come from many friends and fellow workers in the history of science; chief among them are Professor Marie Boas, Dr. Uno Boklund, Dr. Maurice Daumas, Dr. Eduard Farber, M. René Fric, Professor Aaron Ihde, Professor Milton Kerker, Father Patrick John McLaughlin, Professor Robert Schofield, Professor Cyril Stanley Smith, and Dr. Owsei Temkin. Mr. Denis I. Duveen has lent generously from his rich collection of

Lavoisier's books and manuscripts, has discussed with me many aspects of my problem, and has given me the benefit of his deep bibliographical knowledge and wide familiarity with Lavoisier's work.

I am glad, also, to record my appreciation to the members, past and present, of my seminar in the history of science at Cornell who have heard parts of this study presented for their candid and constructive comments. In particular, I wish to thank Miss Rhoda Rappaport and Mr. Roger Hahn for many helpful suggestions and for their careful reading of the manuscript. I assume, of course, full responsibility for the errors of commission and omission that are sure to be called to my attention by others, or that I shall have the dubious pleasure of discovering—too late—for myself.

The final versions of the typescript—the work of Mrs. Anita Reed, Mrs. C. C. Arnold, and Mrs. Robert M. Garcia—were prepared with the help of a subsidy from Cornell's Faculty Research Grants Committee.

Apologies are perhaps due to the reader for my practice of leaving all my citations in the original French; still more, perhaps, for my decision to reproduce all texts exactly as I found them. Thus some citations appear with modernized spelling and punctuation, others as they were printed in the eighteenth century, and still others as they appear in the contemporary manuscripts with their fanciful disregard of punctuation, capitalization, and spelling. In part, I wished to conform with the example set by the editor of the *Correspondance de Lavoisier;* but my principal reason was that I wished to make available to scholars, in the body of the work and in the appendix, all

documents known to me bearing on this phase of Lavoisier's career and to intrude upon them as little as possible.
We have long wished to have these documents brought
together; and those who may be disposed to challenge my
interpretation with my own weapons will find them here
unrusted and with their original temper.

HENRY GUERLAC

December 15, 1960

Contents

Plates

Introduction

IN this study I have tried to shed some light on a particularly obscure, yet especially noteworthy, period in the career of the great French chemist, Antoine-Laurent Lavoisier (1743–1794). We are quite familiar with his early years of scientific apprenticeship, when his interests ranged over a wide variety of scientific problems; and though much is still to be learned about the work of his mature years, there is a substantial literature dealing with Lavoisier's discovery of the role of oxygen, his share in the revision of chemical nomenclature, and other aspects of his massive scientific achievement. But we have understood very imperfectly, if at all, the time of Lavoisier's life when he took the fortunate step of turning to the central problem of combustion. If we cannot know why, and precisely when, he entered on this new path, we will be at a loss to account for one of the truly significant new departures in the history of science.

My primary concern, therefore, has been to determine when, in what manner, and under what influences Lavoisier was led before February, 1773, to the key experiments and generative ideas that touched off the Chemical Revolution. In historical episodes of this importance, a study of origins—even one as detailed as this has turned out to be—needs no special defense. But if my findings can help illuminate the broader problem of the scientific revolution in chemistry (to which our modern age owes so much), the reader may perhaps forgive the rather intricate argument I have been forced to present in this work.

We need hardly stress Lavoisier's pivotal position in the history of chemistry and his role as the chief architect of the Chemical Revolution. He is one of those epoch-making figures in the history of science—like Newton in physics and Darwin in biology—who loom larger than life. If he did not create a new science *ex nihilo,* as some earlier writers believed, he and his disciples nevertheless refashioned the materials, the concepts, and even the language of chemistry so radically that, despite a long and complex early history, the science as we know it to-day seems almost to have been born with him.

Like the political revolution with which it coincided in time, the Chemical Revolution was the work of many hands and the product of diverse forces that are difficult to unravel and assess. Both revolutions were prepared on French soil with materials in part at least—and in the case of the Chemical Revolution quite conspicuously—of British origin. But, as will appear, there were Continental currents related to our problem, influences upon Lavoisier and his contemporaries, which deserve more attention than they have received.[1]

The Chemical Revolution had manifold aspects, and

[1] In a recent paper ("Some French Antecedents of the Chemical Revolution," *Chymia,* 5 [1959], 73–112) I tried to show how the general economic and technical preoccupations of eighteenth-century France promoted an interest in chemistry during Lavoisier's youth and set the stage for the Chemical Revolution.

there have been many diverse attempts to characterize it by a single salient feature. Perhaps I should make explicit how I differ from other writers and what I think chiefly characterizes it, since a recognition of this central feature has served to focus my inquiry and to guide it throughout.

It has long been a cliché of histories of chemistry that Lavoisier's chief contribution was to usher in the age of quantitative chemistry, to enunciate for the first time the principle of the Conservation of Mass in chemical reactions, and to inaugurate the use of the balance. To say the least, this is a gross oversimplification. The so-called Conservation Law—which Dumas, among the earliest, attributed to Lavoisier—had long been a working principle of chemists and had been clearly enunciated at least as early as the first decades of the seventeenth century.[2] From that time onward, the testimony of the balance was increasingly invoked by chemists, especially by the British school—the school of Boyle, Newton, Mayow, and Hales—which sought to develop a "statical," that is

[2] The principle was accepted implicitly by Van Helmont. See Hélène Metzger, *Les doctrines chimiques en France* (Paris, 1923), pp. 177–179. It is clearly stated by Jean Rey in his *Essays* of 1630 (see below, p. 114) and by Francis Bacon in the aphorisms of the *Novum organum* and in the *Sylva sylvarum* (Exp. 100) where he attributes the doctrine to "an obscure writer of the sect of the chemists" (*The Works of Francis Bacon*, ed. James Spedding and R. L. Ellis [Cambridge, 1863], I, 462, and IV, 223). For the views of Newton and his influence on this question, see Hélène Metzger, *Newton, Stahl, Boerhaave et la doctrine chimique* (Paris, 1930), pp. 30–33. The popularity of classical atomism and the new corpuscularianism, with their doctrines of the indestructibility of matter, played an important part in the emergence of this chemical postulate.

to say a quantitative, chemistry akin to physics. By the mid-eighteenth century it was piously hoped that every chemical operation would be performed "in an exact, or geometrical, manner," with the use of accurate balances and weights.[3] For British science, at least, Joseph Black's *Experiments upon Magnesia Alba, Quick-lime, and Some Other Alcaline Substances* (1756) was an admirable exemplification of this method applied with scrupulous care and finesse. But the Continental chemists repeatedly invoked the same ideal, though they lagged somewhat behind their British compeers. In 1766 P. J. Macquer, one of Lavoisier's seniors, applauded the fact that chemistry was beginning to be cultivated "suivant la méthode de la saine Physique."[4] Later, in reporting upon Lavoisier's first book, another French scientist wrote that the author "a soumis tous ses résultats à la mesure, au calcul et à la balance: méthode rigoureuse, qui, heureusement pour l'avancement de la chimie, commence à devenir indispensable dans la pratique de cette science."[5] There is here no suggestion that Lavoisier was doing anything

[3] Peter Shaw, *A New Method of Chemistry; Including the History, Theory, and Practice of the Art: Translated from the Original Latin of Dr. Boerhaave's Elementa Chemiae* (London, 1741), II, 385. This translation of the authorized edition of Boerhaave's famous textbook, containing important notes and additions by Shaw, will be cited henceforth in this study as Shaw-Boerhaave (1741).

[4] *Dictionnaire de chymie, contenant la théorie & la pratique de cette science, son application à la physique, à l'histoire naturelle, à la médecine & à l'économie animale,* etc. (Paris, 1766), II, 326.

[5] *Oeuvres de Lavoisier publiées par les soins de son Excellence le Ministre de l'Instruction Publique et des Cultes* (Paris, 1862–1893), I, 663. This indispensable, though not exhaustive, collection of Lavoisier's memoirs, Academy reports, and occasional papers on various subjects will henceforth be cited as *Oeuvres de Lavoisier.*

novel—only that he was a successful exponent of a method that was proper and up-to-date, but still not widely enough employed. What, in point of fact, Lavoisier did do was to use the balance (and other quantitative techniques as well) with such fidelity and persistence—though not always with rigorous accuracy—that it became in his hands, as Dumas put it so well, "a veritable reagent."[6]

An equally common appraisal of the Chemical Revolution makes it tantamount to the overthrow of the Becher-Stahl phlogistic theory of combustion. But this says at once too much and too little; it exaggerates the break with the past; it neglects the accumulated body of old and recent factual knowledge that was absorbed unaltered by the newer chemistry; and it overlooks the point that something more fundamental occurred than the mere substitution of one theory of combustion for another, centrally important though this proved to be.

There is some truth in all these explanations, but what I believe to be the most significant ingredient in the Chemical Revolution is often overlooked. In the person of Lavoisier two largely separate and distinct chemical traditions seem for the first time to have been merged. At his hands, the pharmaceutical, mineral, and analytical chemistry of the Continent was fruitfully combined with the results of the British "pneumatic" chemists who discovered and characterized the more familiar permanent gases. It was centrally important that for the first time

---

[6] J. B. A. Dumas, *Leçons sur la philosophie chimique* (Paris, 1836), pp. 129–130. In 1778 Macquer wrote: "Ce Physicien [Lavoisier] est venu, les mesures & les balances à la main, donner le sceau de la plus grande authenticité à ces mêmes faits" (*Dictionnaire de chymie* [2nd ed., rev., Paris, 1778], I, 301).

these permanent gases came to be recognized as chemically active participants in very common reactions and
processes. Methodologically, the key to the Revolution
was Lavoisier's systematic application of his special "reagent," the balance, not merely to solids and liquids, but
also to the gases.[7] While the British chemists of the
eighteenth century, following the trail broken by Robert
Boyle, John Mayow, and Stephen Hales, came gradually
to perceive that gases made up a third class of substances
as important to the chemist as solids and liquids, their
work was often more physical than strictly chemical. It
was Lavoisier who most convincingly and systematically
demonstrated—as Black, to be sure, had done for some
special cases and for a particular gas—that this newly
discovered group of substances must be regularly accounted for in strict chemical bookkeeping if the consti-
tution of familiar substances and the nature of familiar
reactions were to be correctly understood. Perhaps it is
not too much to say that the Chemical Revolution—to
hazard a metaphor—supplanted a two-dimensional by a
three-dimensional quantitative chemistry.

The first, and I believe the decisive, step in the Chemical Revolution was Lavoisier's recognition of this new
aerial dimension. But it is clear that this step was taken
well before the discovery of oxygen, and indeed before
Lavoisier suspected that there exist different gases with
different chemical and physical properties. The crucial
event in Lavoisier's career was his realization that air
(which nearly everyone believed to be a simple substance
defined by its physical, rather than by any chemical,

[7] This point is made by Sir Philip Hartog in "The Newer Views of
Priestley and Lavoisier," *Annals of Science*, 5 (1941), 27.

properties) must play a part in chemical transformations —most dramatically those observed in ordinary combustion, the roasting (calcining) of metals, and the reduction of ores or calxes. With all due credit to the British pneumatic chemists, the full appreciation of this crucial fact belongs to Lavoisier alone. Because he kept it constantly in view and used it as the guiding principle of his later research, he could be the first to grasp the significance of the new gas, oxygen, and the first to discover its chemical role, though we now recognize that Scheele and Priestley had independently isolated it before him and noted its most striking properties.

It was, therefore, to discover from what clues, and by what avenues of thought, Lavoisier hit upon this crucial idea of the role of air in combustion that this investigation into the origins of his classic researches was first undertaken. How successful I have been in finding an answer among the scattered and sparse materials (sparse especially from Lavoisier's hand) the reader must, of course, decide for himself.

LAVOISIER—THE CRUCIAL YEAR:

The Background and Origin of His
First Experiments on Combustion in 1772

Plus les faits sont extraordinaires, plus ils s'éloignent des opinions reçues et accréditées, plus il est important de les constater par des expériences répétées et de manière à ne laisser aucun doute. – Lavoisier

CHAPTER 1

Background of the Problem

IT has never been satisfactorily explained just how Lavoisier was led to carry out, in the autumn of 1772, those first experiments on the burning of phosphorus and sulphur and on the reduction of the calx of lead which brought him in succeeding years to the discovery of the role of oxygen, to his antiphlogistic theory of combustion, and to a radical refashioning of the science of chemistry. I believe it is possible, despite the scarcity of documents from Lavoisier's own hand for the period in question, to find a solution to this important historical puzzle. In this study I should like to summarize the evidence—some of it familiar, but some of it new and unpublished—for the interpretation I wish to advance.

I

When Lavoisier, not long after his twenty-ninth birthday, performed the first of his recorded experiments on combustion in the months of September and October, 1772, he was already a scientist of promise who had been a junior member of the Royal Academy of Sciences for something over four years.[1] His list of publications

[1] Lavoisier was born on August 26, 1743. He entered the Academy as *adjoint chimiste surnuméraire* on May 20, 1768. For a survey of

1

was still unimpressive, though hardly a measure of his real accomplishment. Several of the important papers he had presented before the Academy did not appear in print for several years. Chief among these was his famous memoir disproving the presumed transmutation of water into earth, read to the Academy in November, 1770.[2]

---

the biographical literature see my "Lavoisier and His Biographers," *Isis*, 45 (1954), 51–62. Among the books and articles that have appeared since then should be mentioned Maurice Daumas, *Lavoisier, théoricien et expérimentateur* (Paris, 1955); Charles Gillispie, "Notice biographique de Lavoisier par Madame Lavoisier," *Revue d'histoire des sciences et de leurs applications*, 9 (1956), 52–61; and my own article, "A Note on Lavoisier's Scientific Education," *Isis*, 47 (1956), 211–216. The recent book by R. Dujarric de la Rivière and Madeleine Chabrier, *La vie et l'oeuvre de Lavoisier* (Paris, 1959), adds little to our knowledge of Lavoisier's early career. The many illuminating papers by Denis I. Duveen and his collaborators deal largely with the later period of Lavoisier's life. Still the best summary of Lavoisier's work in the autumn of 1772 is Douglas McKie's *Antoine Lavoisier, the Father of Modern Chemistry* (London, 1935), which draws heavily on the pioneer work of A. N. Meldrum.

[2] An anonymous summary of this important work, probably inspired, if not actually drafted, by Lavoisier, appeared in the August, 1771, issue of the Abbé Rozier's newly launched *Observations sur la physique, sur l'histoire naturelle et sur les arts*, a journal in which appeared nearly all the communications Lavoisier published before August, 1772. For these papers see Denis I. Duveen and Herbert S. Klickstein, *A Bibliography of the Works of Antoine Laurent Lavoisier, 1743–1794* (London, 1954), pp. 14–27.

Eighteen issues of Rozier's *Observations* appeared in duodecimo between July, 1771, and December, 1772; beginning with the issue of January, 1773, it was brought out in-4°. The duodecimo volumes of 1771–1772, now of great rarity, were re-issued in 1777 in two quarto volumes under the title *Introduction aux observations sur la physique, sur l'histoire naturelle et sur les arts*. I have used this more readily available re-edition and shall cite it here as *Introduction aux observations*. The journal from 1773 onward will be

Geology was long Lavoisier's central interest, and his early chemical papers—the maiden paper on gypsum and his contributions to water analysis—were obvious by-products of his geological concerns. Even so, there is a certain lack of focus, a certain indecision, perhaps a suggestion of dilettantism, in these first efforts, in many of which we see manifested his practical turn of mind. This early work of Lavoisier has been carefully studied; [3] it is evident from the investigations of A. N. Meldrum that down to 1772—a year that Lavoisier himself took as pivotal in his career [4]—he had displayed no interest in combustion or the calcination of metals and no curiosity about hints in the chemical literature that air might be

cited as *Observations sur la physique;* and for the earlier years, 1773–1776, I have used the reprint edition of 1784–1787, citing the volume number and the original year of publication.

Complete sets of the original duodecimo edition, long inaccessible to scholars, have been located by Professor Douglas McKie. See his discussion in "The *'Observations'* of the Abbé François Rozier (1734–93)—I," *Annals of Science,* 13 (1957), 73–89. A fine duodecimo set has recently been acquired by my friend, Mr. Denis I. Duveen, of New York City, who kindly allowed me to inspect it.

[3] Especially by A. N. Meldrum. See his "Lavoisier's Early Work in Science, 1763–1771," *Isis,* 19 (1933), 330–363, and 20 (1934), 396–425; and his "Lavoisier's Work on the Nature of Water and the Supposed Transmutation of Water into Earth (1768–1773)," *Archeion,* 14 (1932), 246–247. The geological work of Lavoisier has yet to be studied in detail, but cf. Duveen and Klickstein, *op. cit.,* pp. 236–244, and my review of this book, *Isis,* 47 (1956), 85–88. See also Pierre Courte, "Aperçu sur l'oeuvre géologique de Lavoisier," *Annales de la société géologique du Nord,* 69 (1949), 369–375; and R. Dujarric de la Rivière and Madeleine Chabrier, *op. cit.,* pp. 151–158. For the background of Lavoisier's geological work see my "French Antecedents of the Chemical Revolution," *loc. cit.,* pp. 73–112.

[4] *Oeuvres de Lavoisier,* II, 102 and 621.

3

worth the attention of the serious chemist.[5] In support of this conclusion there exists a document which Lavoisier set down in the spring of 1771, when—after having devoted a great part of the two previous years to travels for the Ferme générale—he was free once again to devote himself more particularly to science. In this memorandum, summarized by his biographer, Edouard Grimaux, Lavoisier enumerates the subjects he intends to pursue: researches on niter and indigo, a study of the causes of barometric variation, improvement of his hydrometers, and a revision and completion of his early memoir on the lighting of cities.[6] There is no trace as yet of any interest in combustion, in the role of air, or in the chemistry of phosphorus or sulphur. Yet within little more than a year we find him fully embarked on the most exciting and fruitful investigation of his early career, an investigation combining all these problems and centered upon a theoretical question of fundamental importance.

[5] Fourcroy (A. F. Fourcroy, *Notice sur la vie et les travaux de Lavoisier* [Paris, An IV], p. 27) gave 1770 as the starting point of Lavoisier's work on gases, and he stated elsewhere that Lavoisier's first book, the *Opuscules physiques et chimiques* (1774), contains "une des suites d'expériences auxquelles il s'étoit livré sans relâche depuis les années 1771 & 1772." See *Encyclopédie méthodique— Chimie* (Paris, An IV), III, 416. There is no documentary support for this early date, since it has been shown that the famous memorandum inadvertently dated February, 1772, describing Lavoisier's interest in the chemistry of gases, must actually have been written in 1773. See my "Joseph Priestley's First Papers on Gases and Their Reception in France," *Journal of the History of Medicine and Allied Sciences,* 12 (1957), 1–12; and cf. Max Speter, "Kritisches über die Entstehung von Lavoisiers System," *Zeitschrift für angewandte Chemie,* 39 (1926), 581, a paper that, like the rest of Speter's work, has been undeservedly neglected.

[6] Edouard Grimaux, *Lavoisier, 1743–1794* (2nd ed.; Paris, 1896), p. 34.

4

The Three Notes on Combustion

On November 2, 1772, as everyone familiar with the subject has long known, Lavoisier deposited with the Perpetual Secretary of the Academy of Sciences the famous sealed note (*pli cacheté*), dated the previous day, in which he briefly recorded his momentous discovery that when phosphorus and sulphur are burned they gain markedly in weight because of the "prodigious quantity of air that is fixed during combustion and combines with the vapors." This, he continued, "made me think that what was observed in the combustion of sulphur and phosphorus could well occur in the case of all bodies that gain in weight by combustion and calcination; and I became convinced that the increase in weight of metallic calces was due to the same cause." Lavoisier then described how he had confirmed this conjecture for the case of lead by reducing "litharge" (lead oxide) in a closed vessel, using the "apparatus of M. Hales," and had observed the considerable quantity of air given off at the instant the calx changed into the metal. This discovery seemed to him "one of the most interesting made since Stahl." [7]

In the somewhat altered form Lavoisier gave it for publication, this note has long been known; for many years it provided the earliest record of his work on combustion.[8] But in 1932 two scholars, Max Speter and

[7] In its familiar form this note can be conveniently consulted in *Oeuvres de Lavoisier*, II, 103; an English translation is given by McKie (1935), pp. 117–118. For Lavoisier's use of the terms "litharge" and "minium" see below, p. 160, note 5.

[8] Mentioned by Lavoisier in his *Opuscules* of 1774, the note was first printed in his posthumous *Mémoires de chimie* (Paris, 1805). This is the source of the text as given in the *Oeuvres de Lavoisier*,

A. N. Meldrum, independently published a somewhat earlier note, really the abstract or outline of a memoir—a "memoir-torso," Speter called it—on the combustion of phosphorus. This Lavoisier had asked the Secretary of the Academy, Grandjean de Fouchy, to initial on October 20.[9] A third note, which takes the story somewhat farther back in time, was first published in 1932 by Meldrum.[10] In it Lavoisier recorded that on September 10 of

and as widely cited by Lavoisier scholars. But I have recently called attention to important differences between this version and the original note, which is preserved in the archives of the Academy of Sciences in Paris. For the original note see Appendix VII. The alterations, made by Lavoisier himself in view of publication, do not affect the present discussion. See my "A Curious Lavoisier Episode," *Chymia*, in press.

[9] By Max Speter, "Die entdeckte Lavoisier-'Note' vom 20 Oktober 1772," *Angewandte Chemie*, 45 (1932), 104–107, and soon after by Meldrum, "Lavoisier's Three Notes on Combustion," *Archeion*, 14 (1932), 15–30. Mentioned by Lavoisier in his "Détails historiques, etc." (*Oeuvres de Lavoisier*, II, 104), this document was not brought to light until 1932. The versions given by the two scholars agree closely except for variations in spelling and punctuation and at least two significant differences in reading. See Appendix VI for a corrected transcription.

For the unfortunate exchange between Speter and Meldrum that followed their publication of this document see Speter, "A. N. Meldrum und seine drei 'Noten' Lavoisiers aus dem Jahre 1772," *Archeion*, 14 (1932), 251–252; and Meldrum's reply, *ibid.*, pp. 252–253. Speter's contributions to Lavoisier studies have not been adequately appreciated, even in the sympathetic necrology by Mary Elvira Weeks (*Isis*, 34 [1943], 340–344), where scarcely a word is said about Speter's work on Lavoisier.

[10] This truncated note, from which Marcellin Berthelot quoted a sentence or two in his *La révolution chimique—Lavoisier* ([Paris, 1890], pp. 221–222), was first printed from Lavoisier's small manuscript notebook entitled "Analise de differentes eaux" by Meldrum in "Lavoisier's Three Notes on Combustion," *loc. cit.*, pp. 17–19. Meldrum gives both a facsimile and a transcription. See Appendix V.

6

the same year, having bought from the pharmacist Mitouard an ounce of fine German phosphorus, he used some of it in experiments of a manifestly preliminary character to find out whether this substance absorbed air in burning.

The sequence of Lavoisier's historic experiments in the autumn of that year can be roughly determined by a comparison of these notes. Obviously, the striking behavior of phosphorus was observed at some time between September 10 and October 20, and most probably after the middle of October; for in the *pli cacheté*, where all the results are summarized, he wrote that he had discovered "about eight days ago" that sulphur, like phosphorus, absorbs air and gains weight when burned. This places the sulphur experiment on or about October 24, i.e., shortly after he had set down his results concerning phosphorus. It follows also from this account that the experiments on the reduction of lead oxide were performed between October 24 and November 1, 1772—that is to say, after and presumably as a consequence of his important discovery that when he burned phosphorus and sulphur they absorbed a large amount of air. These facts are quite familiar, and nobody has presumed to doubt that the idea of investigating calcined metals was brought to his mind, in fact was first actually suggested, by the work on phosphorus and sulphur. Indeed, this is what Lavoisier implies in the note of November 1. Understandably, in consequence, all scholars seeking to ascertain the origin of Lavoisier's interest in combustion have confined themselves to searching for clues to his first interest in these substances and their behavior during combustion. The results have not proved convincing.

7

The August Memorandum

Until recently our earliest record of Lavoisier's preoccupation with the phenomenon of combustion has been the brief note of September 10, 1772, recording his purchase of a sample of phosphorus and his preliminary study of this substance. As Douglas McKie once wrote, this note, "so far as we know, marks Lavoisier's first important step in the study of combustion" and shows that at this date, "by some train of thought not now apparent," Lavoisier had determined to find out whether phosphorus absorbed air in burning.[11]

A few years ago the present writer drew attention to a somewhat earlier document which, doubtless because it bore a misleading title, had escaped general notice, though it was readily available in print. So far as I know, the German historian of chemistry, Max Speter, was the first to refer to this document, though he did not fully appreciate its significance.[12] This memorandum, dated August 8, 1772, strongly suggests a different "train of thought" on Lavoisier's part than has usually been attributed to

[11] McKie (1935), pp. 112 and 113.

[12] H. Guerlac, "The Continental Reputation of Stephen Hales," *Archives internationales d'histoire des sciences,* 4 (1951), 393–404; and Max Speter, *Lavoisier und seine Vorläufer* (Stuttgart, 1910), p. 33. Speter devoted more attention to this document in his chapter "Lavoisier" in *Das Buch der grossen Chemiker,* ed. Günther Bugge (Weinheim/Bergstr., 1929), I, 310–312. He was chiefly interested at first in Lavoisier's discussion of the phlogiston theory and wrote: "In seinen Ausführungen (1772) über Elementarfeuer bemerkt er wohl, dass das Wesen des Phlogistons nicht völlig erkannt sei, doch lässt sich hieraus und aus den anderen Darlegungen auch nicht im entferntesten etwa eine Bestreitung der Existenz jenes Phlogistons herauslesen" (*Lavoisier und seine Vorläufer,* p. 33).

8

him.[13] In it Lavoisier seems to hint for the first time, in any document readily available to us, at some dissatisfaction with the phlogiston theory; and in a concluding section, significantly entitled "Sur l'air fixe, ou plutôt sur l'air contenu dans les corps," he considers the possibility that air might combine with metals and mineral substances. He then suggests a way of testing this possibility by experiments in closed vessels using a burning glass and the "appareil de M. Hales," precisely the combination he was to employ three months later in his reduction of lead oxide. These passages constitute an early—though, as we shall see later, perhaps not quite the earliest—record of Lavoisier's interest in the chemical role of air.[14] But of phosphorus or sulphur there is not so much as a mention; it is the calcination and reduction of metals with which he appears to be exclusively concerned in this final section; so it is in connection with the behavior of metals and

[13] "Réflexions sur les expériences qu'on peut tenter à l'aide du miroir ardent," Oeuvres de Lavoisier, III, 261–266. This August memorandum has been incorrectly identified with a "Mémoire sur le feu élémentaire," which Lavoisier is supposed to have read to the Academy on August 19, 1772. Speter and Meldrum accept this false identification, though the latter describes it as "a preliminary note, rather than a memoir" (The Eighteenth Century Revolution in Science, the First Phase [Calcutta, 1930], p. 12). Indeed, it seems to have been a memorandum for Lavoisier's coworkers on the burning-glass experiments and was certainly not read to the Academy. See my "Lost Memoir of Lavoisier," Isis, 50 (1959), 125–129, and below, p. 158.

[14] Cf. Speter's observation: "Man sieht aus dieser Stelle bei Lavoisier schon die ersten gärenden Gedanken über die Rolle der Luft gegenüber den Metallen" (Das Buch der grossen Chemiker, I, 312). Speter, as I believe this study will show, was incorrect when he tentatively attributed this early interest of Lavoisier in the role of air to the debate over Black's work.

mineral substances that he first displays an awareness that air might be a *chemical* participant in combustions and calcinations and not, as nearly everybody believed, merely an indispensable mechanical *instrument,* assisting, as it were physically and externally, the process of burning. With this evidence at hand, we should, I believe, try to answer three questions: First, how did Lavoisier come to speculate, in the summer of 1772, on the possibility that air might play a significant role as a direct participant in chemical change? Second, what could have focused his attention earlier that year upon the problem of combustion? And third, is it possible that the testimony of the sealed note is misleading and that Lavoisier was brought to his *idée maîtresse*—the notion that air might play a chemical role in combustion—by considering the behavior of common mineral substances and the calcination of metals even before he took up the examination of phosphorus and sulphur? In this study I shall be occupied with answering, or attempting to answer, these three questions.

II

It is to the history of pneumatic chemistry, a branch of chemical science almost totally neglected in France but which flourished in England and Scotland in the wake of Robert Boyle's pioneering experiments, that modern scholars have understandably turned to find the answer to our first question concerning the role of air. Obviously, it has usually been assumed, Lavoisier must have been influenced by the work of Boyle's successors; and so the extent of British influence on French chemistry was clearly marked out as a fruitful field of investigation. Surprisingly enough, this influence has only been asserted in general

terms, and what proves to be a complex subject has never
been given the scrupulous and painstaking monographic
treatment it deserves. I cannot pretend to have done so
here, but I shall try, in the pages immediately following,
to provide at least partial answers to the following queries:
(1) Which British pneumatic chemists were known and
cited during Lavoisier's formative years as a chemist?
(2) What attention did their discoveries receive? (3)
When, precisely, were these discoveries appreciated at
their full worth, and what effect did they exert upon
chemical research in France on the eve of Lavoisier's
great experiments?

The Presumed Influence of Joseph Black

It has been commonly, but I believe erroneously, assumed that Lavoisier in 1772 must have been intimately
familiar with British pneumatic chemists—not only with
Stephen Hales, whose profound influence on Lavoisier I
have suggested in earlier studies,[15] but with Joseph Black,
whose classic investigation of the carbonates was published as far back as 1756; with Henry Cavendish, whose
study of Black's "fixed air" and of "inflammable air" was
printed ten years later in the *Philosophical Transactions;*
and perhaps even with Joseph Priestley, for Priestley's
"Observations on Different Kinds of Air," the first important paper in pneumatic chemistry by the man who
was to become Lavoisier's great rival,[16] was read to the
Royal Society early in 1772.

[15] See my "Continental Reputation of Stephen Hales," *loc. cit.*, pp.
393–404; and my "Lavoisier and His Biographers," *loc. cit.*, p. 59.
[16] For the presumed influence of Black see Grimaux, *op. cit.*, p.
101; J. A. Cochrane, *Lavoisier* (London, 1931), p. 50; and McKie

But I have shown elsewhere that Lavoisier could not have seen Priestley's paper until the late spring of 1773 and that it is equally probable that he was unaware of Cavendish's memoir until about the same time.[17] On the other hand, the problem of Joseph Black's influence, or rather lack of it, in France before 1772–1773 is a more complex subject. Although it seems almost incredible that a work we deem so important as Black's *Experiments upon Magnesia Alba,* an elegant model of quantitative experimentation which had appeared in print long before, should have remained almost unknown to Lavoisier's contemporaries, the conclusion is unavoidable that in France, at least, an appreciation of this classic work was long delayed. Fourcroy, Lavoisier's younger disciple, is explicit on this point.[18] Yet most modern scholars have unhesitat-

(1935), pp. 97 and 102. This interpretation seems to go back to Fourcroy, who attributed Lavoisier's inspiration to the "monde nouveau" opened up by Black and his followers: "A peine les premières notions sur les découvertes de Black et de Cavendish sont-elles parvenues en France, et déjà Lavoisier s'étoit empressé de répéter leurs expériences, de les vérifier de diverses manières, de confirmer et d'étendre leurs résultats" (*Notice sur Lavoisier,* p. 27). In a sense, of course, this is true, but only *after* Lavoisier had already embarked on his investigations of air. It is interesting that the alert Meldrum did not fall into this trap, for he writes (*Eighteenth Century Revolution in Science,* p. 3) that the origin of Lavoisier's work in the autumn of 1772 "cannot be traced to Black or Cavendish or Priestley: there is no sign that he had studied what they had done."

[17] Guerlac, "Joseph Priestley's First Papers on Gases," *loc. cit.,* p. 12 and note 30.

[18] After remarking that Black's experiments had been translated into German in 1757, Fourcroy says: "Elles ne furent cependant connues en France & n'y firent naître l'impression qu'elles devoient produire que plus de douze ans après leur publication, & lorsque les discussions savantes sur l'air fixe & les alcalis eurent été le sujet de plusieurs ouvrages très-distingués & l'occasion d'un grand nombre

ingly attributed not only Lavoisier's awareness of the chemical role of air, but sometimes even the quantitative method he displayed in his early study of the water-transmutation problem, to the influence and example of Black's *Experiments*. This could hardly have been the case.

Nevertheless, the silence about Black was not as complete as Fourcroy would have us believe. Though no reliable translation of Black's classic memoir appeared until 1773, French chemists were not left totally in the dark; and, had they been so disposed, they could have learned at least something of Black's theory of causticity and of the role he assigned to "fixed air," i.e., carbon dioxide.

As early as 1758 a severely amputated abridgment of the *Experiments on Magnesia Alba* was published in translation in a French medical journal. It was almost totally ignored, partly because the abstract was too brief to convey the character and importance of Black's method and the cogency of his experimental work, partly because Black's conclusion challenged current beliefs, but also because a derogatory footnote by the editor refuted Black's results on the authority of the much-admired G. F. Rouelle (1703–1770), the teacher of Lavoisier.[19]

d'expériences et de découvertes en Allemagne, en Angleterre & en Hollande" (*Encyclopédie méthodique—Chimie*, III, 365). Fourcroy's date of about 1769 for the introduction of a knowledge of Black's work is certainly too early, yet his general point is valid.

[19] "Expériences Sur la Magnésie; par M. Black, Docteur en Médecine à Edimbourg," *Journal de médecine, chirurgie, pharmacie*, 8 (1758), 254–261. The note in question reads: "M. Rouelle, à qui la Chymie est si redevable, & qui a le premier bien développé l'aetiologie des précipités, démontre que les précipités vrais, tels que ceux dont il est ici question, conservent toujours une petite portion du dissolvant & du précipitant. C'est donc plutôt à eux qu'à l'air qu'on doit attribuer la petite augmentation de poids qui arrive

There is, too, a faint possibility that a complete manuscript translation of Black's *Experiments* was in limited circulation. In 1759 a certain Pierre Demours (the physician who translated Stephen Hales's memoir on ventilators) published a French translation of the first volume (1754) of the *Essays and Observations, Physical and Literary* of the Edinburgh Philosophical Society.[20] Although no translation of the second volume (1756), in which had appeared the important contributions of William Cullen and Joseph Black, seems to have been published, it is possible that a manuscript version of all or part of this second volume was in existence, for Black's memoir seems to have been mentioned before the Academy of Sciences in 1766, in a paper which I shall discuss below.

Be that as it may, the general ignorance of, or indifference to, Black's discoveries in the surprisingly long period between 1758 and 1772 is strikingly evident from a survey of French chemical literature in this period. For example, the chemical articles in those volumes of Diderot's *Encyclopédie* that appeared in the 1760's are silent about "fixed air" and Black's theory of the causticity of alkalis. Even more significant, no mention of Black or his theories can be found in the first edition of P. J. Macquer's authoritative and widely read *Dictionnaire de chymie*, published anonymously in 1766. Indeed, Macquer's failure to refer to the discoveries of Black and his disciples

---

aux métaux qu'on traite de cette manière, & la plupart des autres phénomènes qu'ils présentent dans cet état" (p. 260).

[20] *Essais et observations physiques et littéraires de la Société d'Edimbourg. Traduits de l'anglais* (Paris, 1759). Only this translation of the first volume of the Edinburgh *Essays* is listed in the catalogue of the Bibliothèque Nationale; and Quérard (*France Littéraire*, II, 473) gives only "Tome 1er (et unique). Paris, 1759."

was, as we shall see, the chief criticism leveled against the *Dictionnaire* a few years later by its English translator, James Keir.[21]

Yet in this same year, 1766, appeared the French translations of two books that dealt with certain aspects of the problem of "fixed air." Both of these spoke of Black, but without giving the reader any clear idea of what he had actually done, still less of how he had accomplished it. The first was a French version of David MacBride's *Experimental Essays on Medical and Philosophical Subjects*,[22] a work—as the title suggests—of more medical than chemical interest. MacBride's chief inspiration was Stephen Hales, though he acknowledged his debt to Hales's disciples, the great Doctor Pringle and Joseph Black. He treats Black with respect, and not only briefly summarizes

[21] *A Dictionary of Chemistry. Containing the Theory and Practice of That Science . . . Translated from the French. With Plates, Notes and Additions by the Translator* (2 vols.; London, 1771). This first English edition is listed by Bolton, but not by Ferguson or Duveen. L. J. M. Coleby (*Chemical Studies of P. J. Macquer* [London, 1938], pp. 23 and 42) discusses this work but hopelessly confuses the issue; for although he is aware of Keir's criticism, he nevertheless states that Macquer discussed Black's work on magnesia alba in 1766 under the heading "quick-lime." I can find no such article and no mention of Black in the first French edition of 1766. Macquer did, however, summarize Black's experiments and theories in the articles "Causticité" and "Chaux Terreuse" of the second edition, which appeared in 1777–1778.

[22] *Essais d'expériences. I. Sur la fermentation des mélanges alimentaires. II. Sur la nature & les propriétés de l'air fixe. III. Sur les vertus respectives de différentes espèces d'antiseptiques. IV. Sur le scorbut, etc. Traduits de l'anglois de M. David Macbride par M. Abbadie* (Paris: Chez P. G. Cavelier, 1766). Vincent Abbadie (1737–c.1800) was a surgeon at Bicêtre and to the Duc de Penthièvre, and is known chiefly for this translation. See J. Balteau, ed., *Dictionnaire de biographie française*, I (1933), 48–49.

Black's theory of causticity, but gives the few facts commonly known about his "fixed air." His purpose, however, was not primarily to investigate gases but to prove experimentally a theory he attributed to Hales and to Albrecht von Haller that air is "the *true cement* which binds together the earthy particles of bodies."[23] Above all, he wished to demonstrate, in the interests of the medical art, the preservative, antiseptic, and restorative properties of fixable air.

The other book made known to the French in 1766 was Johann Friedrich Meyer's *Chymische Versuche*.[24] Meyer, a German apothecary, elaborated at great length in this book his largely forgotten theory that alkalis are rendered caustic by the addition of an acidic principle he called *causticum* or *acidum pingue,* and that they become mild when it is lost. Although Meyer gave the reader some general ideas about Black's work, he did so largely by way of

[23] David MacBride, Surgeon, *Experimental Essays* (London, 1764), p. 28. Sir John Pringle (1707–1782), an outstanding physician and later a friend of Franklin and Priestley, was famous for studies of putrefaction which appeared in the *Philosophical Transactions* for 1750 (vol. 46, no. 495, p. 480, and no. 496, pp. 425 and 550). See Dorothea Waley Singer, "Sir John Pringle and His Circle," *Annals of Science,* 6 (1949), 127–180 and 229–261. The full English title quoted above is that of the second edition (1767).

[24] *Chymische Versuche zur näheren Erkenntniss des ungelöschten Kalchs, der elastischen und elektrischen Materie des allerreinsten Feuerwesens und der ursprünglichen allgemeinen Säure nebst einem Anhange von den Elementen* (Hanover and Leipzig, 1764).

The French translation is entitled *Essais de Chymie, sur la chaux vive, la matière élastique et électrique, le feu, et l'acide universel primitif; Avec un Supplément sur les Elémens. Traduits de l'Allemand de M. Frederich Meyer, Apothicaire à Osnabruck. Par M. P. F. Dreux, Ancien Apothicaire Aide-Major des Armées du Roi en Allemagne* (2 vols.; Paris: Chez G. Cavelier, 1766).

16

an elaborate and apparently convincing refutation of it.

Neither MacBride's book on the medical use of fixed air nor Meyer's ambitious monograph on the causticity problem was an adequate vehicle for transmitting much knowledge about Black's discoveries, still less for conveying any idea of his experimental genius; indeed, though we know both books to have been in Lavoisier's library, neither one aroused much curiosity in France until some years later. There was, however, an interesting reaction to MacBride's book which we may note at this point.

Late in 1766, at meetings held in November and December, a Parisian apothecary, J. F. Demachy (1728–1803), read before the Academy of Sciences a memoir entitled "Recherches sur quelques propriétés accordées à l'Air." Although not a member of the Academy—he had been an unsuccessful aspirant the previous spring—Demachy was a well-known figure.[25] A pupil of the elder Rouelle and a devoted adherent of the phlogiston theory of Stahl, he had earned a reputation as a competent pharmacist, a teacher of chemistry, and a translator of various German works of Stahl's discples. In this memoir on air, Demachy gives the results of thirty-six experiments—pretty much repetitions and variations of those of Hales and Mac-Bride—which convinced him that air cannot be fixed in bodies, as these authorities believed.[26] The air given off by bodies in fermentation, chemical effervescence, or distillation Demachy thought was always produced by the con-

[25] For Demachy (also sometimes given as De Machy) see Hermann Kopp, *Geschichte der Chemie* (Braunschweig, 1843–1847), II, 131; and the sketch by Toraude in J.-F. Demachy, *Histoires et contes, précédés d'une étude historique, anecdotique et critique sur sa vie et ses oeuvres*, ed. L.-G. Toraude (Paris, 1907), pp. v–cviii.

[26] *Observations sur la physique*, 7 (1776), 301–304.

17

version of water into air; in the same fashion he explained the supposed absorption or "fixation" of air by bodies through the transformation of air into water. The chemical peculiarities of this so-called "fixed air," such as its characteristic odor and piquancy and its ability to precipitate limewater, he attributed to acid vapors released in some mysterious fashion when the water is transformed into air.[27] Thus Demachy was convinced that the partisans of fixed air had misinterpreted their results. Concerning these British pneumatic chemists he wrote:

M. Black membre de la société d'Edimbourg, ajouta à cette hypothese [the Hales doctrine of fixable air], que certaines substances, & entr'autres les terres calcaires, telles que la magnésie, la craie & la chaux, avoient la propriété d'attirer cet air fixe, lorsque par la calcination on les en avoit privées, & il imagina que tous les phénomenes des chaux vive & éteinte, étoient dus à la présence de cet air fixe, ou à son absence. M. Macbride de Dublin, a cru démontrer l'action de cet air fixe en suivant l'idée de M. Black.[28]

This summary of Black's ideas—the earliest, so far as I know, to be presented before the Academy of Sciences— could perhaps have been derived from reading MacBride or Meyer; but what is interesting is that Demachy's reference to Black is footnoted: "Voyez Tome II. Mémoires d'Edimbourg, traduits par M. Demours." Since no such sec-

---

[27] It is not surprising that Demachy later published a supposed refutation of Lavoisier's famous experiment on the conversion of water into earth, for he clearly believed in the interconvertibility of the elements. See his *Recueil de dissertations physico-chymiques* (Amsterdam, 1774), pp. 416–425.

[28] *Observations sur la physique*, 7 (1776), p. 302.

ond volume, as I have already suggested, seems ever to have been published, I can only assume that either Demachy had seen a manuscript version of Demours' translation of the second volume or that—quite reprehensibly—he cited it in expectation of its appearance, basing his information about Black on his other sources.

Demachy's paper, though it strikes a modern reader as an inconclusive bit of experimentation, nevertheless received a favorable report from the *rapporteurs*, the Abbé Nollet and Macquer, who recommended that it appear in the so-called *Mémoires des savants étrangers*, an intermittent publication which printed selected memoirs of scientists, both foreign and domestic, who were not members of the Academy. Actually the memoir never appeared in this series (of which eleven volumes appeared between 1750 and 1786) and was only published (in Rozier's *Observations*) ten years after it was read. It is neither historically nor scientifically of much importance, but it does serve to call our attention to the sort of prejudice that stood in the way of an acceptance of, or even much curiosity about, the theories of Black and Mac-Bride.

Behind Demachy's attack on the ideas of Hales, Black, and MacBride, there can be discerned a widespread objection to admitting that air could be a constitutive principle of chemical substances. This prejudice was held by the more rigorous disciples of Stahl, despite the influence the ideas of Stephen Hales began to exert by the middle of the eighteenth century in France. In general, it can be said that, unlike their British confrères, the Continental chemists had remained largely indifferent to the suggestive discoveries of Van Helmont and Boyle on the subject of gases, vapors, and airs produced by chemical reaction and had focused almost exclusively on the behavior of solids and liquids, giving vapors, effervescenes, and ebullitions only scant attention. This neglect of air was perhaps not unconnected with the widespread abandonment, in the later seventeenth century, of the Aristotelian theory of the Four Elements. In its place, some had adopted Van Helmont's theory of water as the ultimate principle; some followed J. J. Becher in combining this with a theory of three earth elements; still others expanded the Paracelsian *tria prima* into a five-element theory. In many of these schemes one can discern the Earth, Water, and Fire of the peripatetic theory retained in various transparent disguises, when not openly assigned an elementary role. But the element Air is in each of these theories conspicuously absent; to it, in fact, had been exclusively relegated the duties of a *physical* agent or instrument.

Influenced by the seventeenth century's mechanical philosophy and more specifically by Robert Boyle's classic study of the physical properties of air, a doctrine commonly held during the early eighteenth century, the Instrumental Theory, transformed the old Four Elements into the four *instruments,* mechanical agencies which were thought to produce, sustain, or transfer the intestine motion upon which all chemical change was in some manner ultimately believed to depend. Water, air, and fire—though the first and last were usually understood to play a chemical role as well—were described as the chief instruments of motion. Earth, besides being an element, embodied the principle of rest and aggregation. Atmospheric air and water were, of course, effective as *menstrua,* i.e., solvents, with the property of conveying motion to bodies.

20

But fire was obviously the most violent impelling agent, the truly active and proper instrument at the disposal of the chemist. By this instrumental doctrine writers like Stahl and Boerhaave seem to have wished to create a physical foundation for chemistry, a unified interpretation of their science which linked it with the mechanical philosophy.[29]

In Boerhaave's early instrumental theory air—*qua* air —was only a physical agent, producing its varied effects by its weight, its elasticity, its capacity for producing and sustaining motion, and its role as a great menstruum or solvent.[30] If atmospheric air seemed to exert chemical effects, this was only because it was a "chaos," containing a great variety of effluvia and active foreign particles. According to Boerhaave, air is necessary for combustion, not because of the action of these impurities, as Sendivogius and others believed who adopted the theory of an aerial niter, but because its pressure keeps the flame alive, providing a "fornax or vault" to retain the oily matter (the *pabulum ignis*) which feeds the flame. Air is not itself,

[29] For Stahl's version of the instrumental theory see his *Specimen Beccherianum* (Leipzig, 1703), pp. 32–33, and his *Fundamenta chymiae* (Nuremberg, 1746–1747), 1, 36–43. The first edition of this work appeared in 1723; an abridged translation by Peter Shaw (G. E. Stahl, *Philosophical Principles of Universal Chemistry* [London, 1730]) gives the discussion of instruments on pp. 3–9. There is an elaborate exposition in the unauthorized edition of Boerhaave's lectures: *Institutiones et experimenta chemiae* (Paris, 1724). According to William Burton (*Account of the Life and Writings of Herman Boerhaave* [2nd ed.; London, 1746]) the English translation by Peter Shaw and E. Chambers (*A New Method of Chemistry* [London, 1727]) is a more reliable source of Boerhaave's early views than the Latin edition of 1724, for various manuscripts were compared in making the translation.

[30] *A New System of Chemistry*, pp. 295–304.

21

Boerhaave insisted, the soul of fire or the pabulum of fire, but a purely physical agent in combustion.[31]

In Stahl's chemistry two of the instrumental substances, earth and water, doubled as elements or constituents of matter, but air was deemed to be chemically inert. It was at first a corollary of the instrumental theory that air is incapable of combining with, or being chemically fixed in, solid or liquid substances. This view, which Van Helmont had foreshadowed with his doctrine that water was the only principle [32]—a doctrine which was reflected in Becher's theory—was explicitly stated by Stahl,[33] who even attributed chemical ebullitions and effervescences to a release of water in the form of vapor.[34] This belief in the chemical inactivity of air was favored by Stahlians of the strict observance, like Demachy. Even Boerhaave, who had so little in common with Stahl, at least agreed with him on this point, or at all events did for a time; later, however, he was to alter his opinion.

This persisting point of view, though soon challenged by the findings of Stephen Hales in a manner which I

[31] *Ibid.*, p. 270. And we read: "Air has a very great effect in the varying of fire: thus the heavier the air is, the more violently fire burns; and the lighter, the less: in *vacuo* it scarce burns at all" (p. 268).

[32] Metzger, *Newton, Stahl, Boerhaave,* p. 113.

[33] "Elastica illa expansio aeri ita per essentiam propria est, ut nunquam ad vere densam aggregationem nec ipse in se, nec in ullis mixtionibus coivisse sentiri possit" (cited by Lavoisier, *Oeuvres,* I, 464, from Stahl's *Experimenta, Observationes, Animaversiones, CCC Numero, Chymicae Et Physicae* [Berlin, 1731]). Cf. Metzger, *Newton, Stahl, Boerhaave,* p. 113.

[34] *Traité des sels . . . Par George-Ernest Stahl: Traduit de l'Allemand* (Paris, 1771), pp. 360–363. This translation was made by the Baron d'Holbach.

shall shortly describe, accounts in some measure for the cavalier dismissal by many French chemists of their first scant knowledge of the work of Black and MacBride. But the absence of a complete translation of Black's work was probably even more important, for at least some French scientists were predisposed, by a knowledge of Hales's discoveries, to believe that air might take part in chemical reactions.

At all events it is hardly surprising that as late as the summer of 1772 the ambitious young chemist, Lavoisier, though he had come to suspect the chemical importance of air, did not know much more than the name of Joseph Black, if indeed he had ever heard of him. He clearly had not read, let alone studied, Black's *Experiments upon Magnesia Alba;* for this the memorandum of August 8 supplies conclusive evidence. At one point in this document Lavoisier wrote:

Il paraît constant que l'air entre dans la composition de la pluspart des minéraux, des métaux même et en très-grande abondance. Aucun chimiste cependant n'a fait encore entrer l'air dans la définition ni des métaux ni d'aucun corps minéral.[35]

Clearly, then, this early evidence that Lavoisier was thinking about the chemical role of air cannot be traced to the influence of Black. Had he known Black's work— directly or, as Speter believed, through the memoir of Black's Viennese disciple, Jacquin, published in 1769—it is hard to imagine how he could have written the last sen-

[35] *Oeuvres de Lavoisier,* III, 266. For a discussion of this August memorandum, printed in its original form in Appendix III, see below, pp. 88–90 and 102–104.

tence; for to show that air enters into the "definition," that is the composition, of mineral substances is precisely what Black had accomplished with such consummate elegance.[36] And though Lavoisier's first sentence, with its reference to air obtained from metals, may seem to imply some knowledge of other writings on gases, such as Cavendish's careful study of "inflammable air" (hydrogen) obtained by the action of dilute acid on metals, Lavoisier is merely referring to what, for a long time, had been commonly observed in the laboratory.[37]

[36] See my "Joseph Black and Fixed Air: A Bicentenary Retrospective, with Some New or Little Known Material," *Isis*, 48 (1957), 124–151 and 433–456. Cf. Speter, "Lavoisier," *Das Buch der grossen Chemiker*, I, 312. It is significant that in 1772 Antoine Baumé, though well acquainted with Hales's work on fixed air, was totally ignorant of Black's experiments. This is evident from the discussion of quicklime and causticity in his *Chymie expérimentale et raisonnée* (Paris, 1773), I, 161–195. At one point he writes: "Les pierres calcaires doivent contenir de l'air. . . . J'ignore, au reste, si on a fait des expériences pour démontrer l'existence de l'air dans cette espèce de terre qui doit nécessairement en contenir, puisqu'elle a fait autrefois partie des animaux: c'est la matière d'un très beau travail à faire" (pp. 173–174). Elsewhere he shows no understanding of the nature of the "pellicule ou crême de chaux" (pp. 179–180). He has, however, heard of Meyer's theory of *acidum pingue*, for he objects to a term that he says merely designates the phlogiston which is in quicklime (p. 152). Sage, in the discussion of limestone and quicklime in his *Elémens de minéralogie docimastique* (Paris, 1772), also shows himself unaware of Black's work.

[37] Hales had measured the air produced by the action of dilute oil of vitriol on iron filings and had of course assumed that the air came from the metal itself. See his *Vegetable Staticks* (London, 1727), Exper. XCIV, p. 217. Sage, in the work just cited, devotes two pages to describing the "vapeurs" produced by the action of different acids on iron or iron filings, distinguishing the odorless, inflammable "vapors" produced by the action of dilute vitriolic acid or marine acid (HCl) on iron, from the red, noninflammable vapor produced

III

The Rev. Stephen Hales is the only pneumatic chemist Lavoisier mentioned by name before February, 1773. Hales's name appears in the August memorandum and in the sealed note of November 1, and he heads the list of pneumatic chemists with whose achievements Lavoisier had become at least somewhat familiar when he set down his February memorandum.[38] There was real justification for this interest in Hales.

In his *Vegetable Staticks* (1727) Hales had included a long, important, but seemingly unrelated, chapter called the "Analysis of Air." Here he described an array of experiments in which he measured the air produced by subjecting a variety of substances to fermentation, destructive distillation, and the action of strong reagents. (Figs. 1 and 2.) He became convinced that air was in some manner fixed, with loss of its characteristic elastic properties, in all organic and many inorganic materials. Hales's book had a remarkable success and was widely quoted.[39] One of the earliest chemists to be influenced by the chemical chapter of the *Vegetable Staticks* was Boerhaave. If

---

when iron is treated with nitric acid. Unlike Hales (and Lavoisier) he does not speak of air, and he assumed vapors to be quite different from air (*Elémens de minéralogie docimastique*, pp. 198–199).

[38] In the memorandum of February 20, 1773, Lavoisier wrote: "Quelque nombreuses que soient les expériences de MM. Hales, Black, Magbride [Mac Bride], Jacquin, Cranz [Crantz], Pristley [Priestley] et de Smeth, sur cet objet, il s'en faut bien néanmoins qu'elles soient assez nombreuses pour former un corps de théorie complet." See Berthelot, *Révolution chimique*, pp. 47–48 and Appendix VIII.

[39] See my "Continental Reputation of Stephen Hales," *loc. cit.*, pp. 393–404.

we can take the spurious edition of his chemical lectures, published without his consent in 1724, to represent his early views, Boerhaave at first shared the view that air was chemically inert and a purely physical agent. When he brought out the authorized version of his *Elementa chemiae* in 1732, a work which—to the exasperation of the Stahlians in France—had a resounding success and a prolonged influence, we find Boerhaave reluctant to abandon the instrumental doctrine; for in a greatly expanded section on air he elaborates at some length on its role as a purely physical agent.[40] But near the end of this section he turns his attention to the recent findings of Hales, which he has confirmed with an apparatus somewhat superior to Hales's in that it eliminated, as Lavoisier later pointed out, all contact of the gas evolved with water. The reactions were carried out in an evacuated receptacle supplied with a mercury pressure gauge, and by applying Boyle's law Boerhaave was able to convert his results to the equivalent volume at atmospheric pressure for comparison with the Englishman's data. He concludes this section with the following important passage:

Indeed, nearly all sorts of bodies, treated by fire, shew, that elastic air makes a considerable part in their composition; at least, that all known bodies do, by the force of fire, separate a fluid, elastic, compressible matter, that contracts with cold and expands with heat, which are the properties of elastic air; tho' this matter, when confined and bound down in bodies, does not produce the effects of air; but when once let loose, it has all the effects of air, and may again enter as an ingredient in the composition of other bodies. Chemistry clearly shews this man-

[40] *Elementa chemiae* (Leyden, 1732), pp. 161 ff.

26

ner of resolution and combination: and no examples hereof need at present be produced, after what Dr. *Hales* hath written upon the subject in his vegetable statics.[41]

Boerhaave was notably cautious about asserting that the air produced in these reactions is contained in the original substances as "a considerable part in their composition." Indeed, his treatment of air, if we take the work as a whole, is a confusing combination of his earlier views with his cautious adoption of Hales's findings. Other chemists must have reacted as did Lavoisier, who later wrote:

Le célèbre Boerhaave . . . ne s'est pas toujours parfaitement accordé avec lui-même sur la combinaison et la fixation de l'air: tantôt il semble nier que l'air puisse se combiner dans les corps et contribuer à la formation de leurs parties solides; tantôt il semble adopter l'opinion contraire et se ranger du côté de M. Hales. Enfin, en rapprochant ce que dit ce célèbre auteur dans différents endroits de ses ouvrages, on voit clairement que les expériences de M. Hales, quand elles parurent, lui firent changer de sentiment, et qu'il adopta jusqu'à un certain point le système de la fixation de l'air dans les corps: mais, sans doute, en même temps, que cette théorie ne lui parut pas suffisamment démontrée pour l'obliger à retrancher de ses ouvrages ce qu'il avait dit de contraire.[42]

[41] Shaw-Boerhaave, I, 434.

[42] *Oeuvres de Lavoisier*, I, 461. Lavoisier's feeling about Boerhaave's indecision may have been enhanced by his possession of copies both of the spurious edition of 1724 and of Allamand's French translation (1754) of the authorized *Elementa chemiae*. In these two versions Boerhaave's treatment of air is markedly different. For the influence of Hales on Boerhaave see Milton Kerker: "Herman Boerhaave and the Development of Pneumatic Chemistry," *Isis*, 46 (1955), 36–49.

Despite Boerhaave's hesitations, and despite the opposition of Stahlians of the strict observance like Demachy, many persons came to believe that Hales had shown that air could be a constituent of bodies, or at least was held in them in an inelastic state. This view rapidly gained supporters on the Continent when the *Vegetable Staticks* was translated into Dutch, German, Italian, and French. Buffon's French translation in 1735 was a particularly influential and popular book. Everywhere, including France, Hales was cited more frequently for his chemical chapter, which seemed to challenge accepted opinion with a battery of carefully conducted experiments, than for those elegant physiological studies on plants and animals by which he is chiefly remembered today. If men like Demachy and Guyton de Morveau sought to disprove his findings, others—among them Musschenbroek, Venel, Voltaire, Macquer, Baumé, and the Abbé Rozier—approvingly cited his discoveries concerning fixable air.[43]

[43] As a supplement to my "Continental Reputation of Stephen Hales," *loc. cit.*, pp. 398–402, it may be mentioned that Hales is cited for his work on air by Voltaire in his "Conseils à un journaliste" (*Oeuvres*, ed. Moland, XXIII, 242); by Venel in the papers to be discussed below (p. 65) and in his article "Effervescence" in the *Encyclopédie*, V (1755), 404–405; by Macquer in his *Dictionnaire de chymie* (ed. 1766), I, 58–59; by Antoine Baumé in his *Manuel de chymie* (Paris, 1763), pp. 21, 47–48, 52–53; and several times by the Abbé Rozier in his prize-winning paper in the volume *De la fermentation des vins, et de la meilleure manière de faire l'eau-de-vie* (Lyon, 1770), *passim*. There are scattered references to Hales's work on air in P. van Musschenbroek, *Essai de physique*, trans. P. Massuet (Leyden, 1751). For a reference by Cisternay Du Fay, who admired Hales, see I. Bernard Cohen, *Franklin and Newton* (Philadelphia, 1956), pp. 247 and 255–257.

Lavoisier owned a copy of Buffon's 1735 translation of Hales's *Vegetable Staticks*. It is listed in the "Bibliothèque de Madame la

Whether Lavoisier read the *Vegetable Staticks* before 1772 cannot be determined, but there is no doubt that he was familiar with its main findings and conclusions. If in no other way, he must have learned about Hales from his master, G. F. Rouelle, who regularly spoke of Hales's experiments in the well-attended public lectures he gave for so many years in the amphitheater of the Jardin du Roi,[44] and who was accustomed to repeat some of them. Rouelle had even devised a successful and widely copied improvement of the Englishman's apparatus for measuring the quantity of air released or absorbed in various reactions.[45] What he did, in effect, was to combine two of Hales's devices—the pedestal apparatus and the device for collecting gases over water (see Fig. 3).

Comtesse de Rumford," I, Catalogue, p. 91. This list of books once belonging to Lavoisier is in the possession of Mr. Denis I. Duveen, who has kindly allowed me to consult it.

[44] *Cours de chymie de M*[r]. *Rouelle rédigé par M*[r]. *Diderot & éclairci par plusieurs notes*, MS 564–565, Bibliothèque de Bordeaux. See especially I, 108–109; II, 125, 207–208; and III, 281–282. In his earliest printed notice of Hales, Lavoisier writes: "Ces expériences [on the production of air] sont trop constantes pour pouvoir révoquées en doute, elles ont, d'ailleurs, été répétées un grand nombre de fois, aux yeux de tout le public, dans les leçons de M. Rouelle" (*Oeuvres de Lavoisier*, II, 7). The passage occurs in Lavoisier's "Premier mémoire sur la nature de l'eau," but it was probably added in his revision of 1773 and did not form part of the memoir as he presented it to the Academy in November, 1770.

[45] Lavoisier refers in his *Opuscules* to the pedestal apparatus "dont l'idée vient originairement de M. Hales, qui a été, depuis, corrigé par feu M. Rouelle" (*Oeuvres de Lavoisier*, I, 601). Rozier used a modification of "la machine de Hales" for his experiments on wine (*op. cit.*, p. 78); so also did Pierre Bayen, who spoke of using, probably in 1772–1773, "un de ces appareils chimico-pneumatiques, dont *Hales* passera toujours pour être l'inventeur, quelle que soit la forme que nous puissions leur donner" (*Opuscules chimiques de*

Fig. 1. Stephen Hales's pedestal apparatus for measuring the amount of air given off or absorbed by the respiration of small animals or by substances ignited on the pedestal by means of a burning glass. At the start of the experiment, air is withdrawn from the cylinder by a siphon or bellows until the water rises to a chosen level. The amount of air given off or absorbed is measured by the change in the water level.

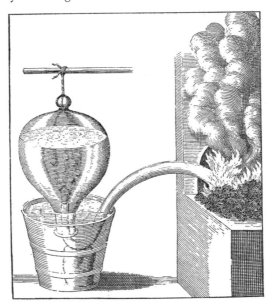

Fig. 2. Hales's gun barrel apparatus for collecting over water the gases produced by destructive distillation. It is the ancestor of the pneumatic trough perfected by Henry Cavendish and Joseph Priestley.

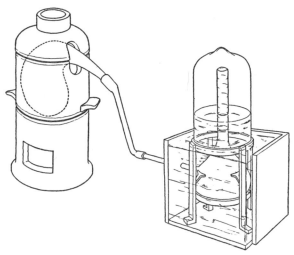

Fig. 3. G. F. Rouelle's combination of Hales's two devices. A distillation flask, placed in a furnace, is connected by a bent tube to a receiving flask. This receiver, with a long neck marked by graduations, is held in a metal frame surmounted by a ring and placed in a container filled with water. A glass bell jar is supported inside the ring. From this the air is withdrawn until the water rises almost to the top of the receiver neck. When the furnace is lighted, the gases pass through the neck of the receiver into the bell jar forcing down the water level. The volume of the gas given off is roughly estimated by the drop in the water level as shown by the graduations on the neck of the receiver.

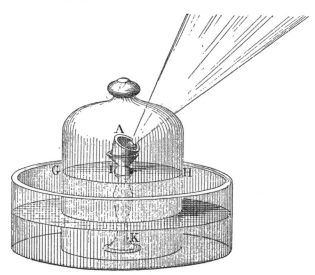

Fig. 4. Lavoisier's adaptation of Hales's pedestal apparatus.

It was largely Hales's influence, too, which led Rouelle to depart in some important respects from the Stahlian doctrines that he is so justly credited with making popular in France. On one important point Rouelle's chemical theory differed notably from Stahl's.[46] Whereas Stahl had taught that two of the four instruments—earth and water —entered into chemical combination, Rouelle believed that all four substances were not only instruments, but also chemical reactants. Though his views were not always consistent, Stahl seems to have thought of phlogiston as a substance distinct from fire, in fact as one of Becher's three earths, and as possessing weight. But Rouelle taught that phlogiston was the "matter of fire," or the instrument fire entering into chemical combination. More important still, air also had this double function in Rouelle's scheme. It is first of all an instrument, whose essential property is its elasticity. Indeed, Rouelle attempted to explain the distillation of liquids by the mechanical action of air; vapors—which he sharply distinguishes from air because they are expansible but not compressible, and therefore not truly elastic—are carried up when air expands and condensed in the recipient when the air cools and contracts. Yet Rouelle did not doubt that air was contained

Pierre Bayen [Paris, An VI], II, 7). For Rouelle's modification of Hales's apparatus see the description in Fourcroy, _Encyclopédie méthodique—Chimie_, II (1792), 354; also III (An IV), 409–410. For a drawing of Rouelle's apparatus see _ibid._, VI (1815), Fig. 45, Pl. XVII. Rouelle had perfected his apparatus by 1761. See the _Avant-coureur_ for December 21, 1761, pp. 802–805.

[46] This aspect of Rouelle's work has been explored by Miss Rhoda Rappaport in her thesis for the degree of Master of Arts, entitled "G.-F. Rouelle, His _Cours de chimie_ and Their Significance for Eighteenth Century Chemistry" (Cornell University, 1958), especially chap. iii.

in many substances, as corpuscles interspersed among those of other bodies and deprived of that elasticity which was the characteristic property of air in bulk. He regularly demonstrated to his audience the great quantity of air produced by the destructive distillation of organic substances and pointed out that the harder kinds of wood—and such compacted animal materials as bones, ivory, and teeth—produce more air than softer tissues: an echo, perhaps, of the theory that air is a kind of cement holding the parts of bodies together.[47] Air produced by fermentation, destructive distillation, or combustion is often mixed with vapors, some of which are inflammable and others—like Van Helmont's *gas sylvestre*—noxious to life. This *gas sylvestre,* which Rouelle thought identical with, or very similar to, the vapor produced by burning coal, was not deemed a kind of air but described as an extremely attenuated acid, united with phlogiston. Such vapors could be separated from air by passing the air through water.[48]

The most surprising by-product of Hales's influence was a revival among French chemists of the theory of the Four Elements, foreshadowed in this theory of Rouelle. Since air had been shown to be a constituent of matter, perhaps fire might also exist, not only free, but in a "fixed and concrete" form, as Buffon, among others, suggested. Macquer, in particular, believed Hales to have produced overwhelming proof that air was a common constituent of matter. He took this as evidence that chemistry was returning to the Aristotelian Four Elements, since there was little doubt that earth, water, and fire (phlogiston) "entrent véritablement comme principes dans la composition

[47] *Cours de chymie de M^r. Rouelle,* Bordeaux MS, II, 208.
[48] *Ibid.*

33

des corps." [49] Early in his career Lavoisier, as we shall discover, was to make significant use of this theory.

It should, therefore, occasion no surprise to learn that it was through Hales—indirectly from Boerhaave, Rouelle, Macquer, and others, if not directly through a reading of the *Vegetable Staticks*—that Lavoisier came to appreciate the important role that air might play in chemical processes; that he adapted Hales's pedestal apparatus for one of his first important experiments on combustion; that he could think of no greater praise of Priestley's first important work on gases than to compare the author to Hales; and finally that he recommended the *Vegetable Staticks* to his readers in 1774 as "un fonds presque inépuisable de méditation." [50]

But if Lavoisier, like other French chemists—those who

[49] *Dictionnaire de chymie* (ed. 1766), II, 328–329. Baumé seems to have been of the same opinion, for he wrote somewhat earlier: "On doit regarder, avec les meilleurs Chymistes & Physiciens, l'eau, le feu & la terre comme les élémens ou les vrais principes primitifs des corps. A ces trois principes, on peut ajouter l'air; les expériences de Boile, & surtout celles que rapporte M. Halles [*sic*] dans sa Statique des Végétaux, indiquent au moins que cet élément fait partie de beaucoup de corps composés, & qu'il est un des principes constituans des corps organisés" (*Manuel de chimie* [Paris, 1763], p. 21). This passage is reproduced unaltered in the second edition of 1765, p. 23. In 1774 Lavoisier wrote that Hales had shown that air "doit être compté au nombre des principes chimiques et occuper un rang qu'on lui avait refusé jusqu'alors" (*Oeuvres de Lavoisier*, I, 460). But earlier, in 1766, he held a different view. After reading two memoirs of Euler on the elements, he had written: "L'air n'est pas un élément qui existe par lui-même, c'est un être composé, c'est l'eau réduite en vapeur ou pour parler d'une manière plus intelligible, c'est le resultat de la combinaison de l'eau avec la matière du feu" (cited by Daumas, *Lavoisier, théoricien et expérimentateur*, p. 26).

[50] *Oeuvres de Lavoisier*, I, 456 and 512.

34

accepted Hales's views and those who did not—had long been familiar with the "Analysis of Air," it is evident that something must have occurred in the months before Lavoisier wrote the August memorandum to give new meaning to the half-century-old experiments of the English parson. In the first place, as we shall see in more detail farther on, Lavoisier had been puzzling at just this time about a chemical phenomenon, the reduction and calcination of metals, recently put into a new light by the work of a provincial chemist, and about the cause of effervescences. In the second place, it was precisely in the years 1771–1772 that the chemists of Paris had their attention urgently called to the important work on gases being carried out in Britain by the followers of Hales and to the strenuous debates these discoveries and theories had aroused in Germany and Holland. We must stop to consider, at this point, the chain of events which introduced a knowledge of the later pneumatic chemistry into France, launching what Fourcroy later called the "discussions savantes" on "fixed air" and alkalis and opening what Bayen described as "l'époque où la question de l'air fixe commençoit à occuper tous les chimistes." [51]

[51] See above, this chapter, note 18, and *Opuscules chimiques de Pierre Bayen*, II, 1–2, note.

CHAPTER 2

The Introduction of Pneumatic Chemistry into France

IT is not hard to identify with some precision the path by which knowledge of the new discoveries on gases came to France from Britain or to point to the two men who were the humble agents in this historically significant transaction, who repeatedly insisted on the importance of the recent British experiments, and who transmitted the necessary books and information to the chemists of the Royal Academy of Sciences in Paris. The real instigator was that picaresque and largely neglected personage, João Jacinto de Magalhães (1722–1790), a Portuguese savant living in London, whose main channel of communication with French scientists was his patron and correspondent, Trudaine de Montigny (1733–1777), a worthy civil servant and *membre honoraire* of the Academy.

Magalhães—or Magellan, to use the form of his name he favored after leaving Portugal—had been born in Aveiro of a family boasting descent from the famed navigator.[1] Educated for the clergy, he early entered a congregation of Augustinian monks at Coimbra; he was thirty-one when he made the acquaintance of the French naval officer and astronomer, Gabriel de Bory (1720–1801), when the latter visited Portugal to observe a solar eclipse. Bory was received at the monastery of Coimbra and was struck by the scientific enthusiasm of the monks, especially of Magellan, who served as his guide and with whom he formed a lasting friendship. It was sometime after 1755 that Magellan, perhaps stimulated by this contact with the outside world, sought permission to leave the order and put the scientific backwater of Coimbra behind him. After a stay in Paris, interrupted by short trips to other European countries, he took up residence in London about 1764; here he lived, except for brief excursions to the Continent, until his death in 1790.

This former cleric, described by an English contemporary as a tall and bony man, "plain in his dress, unaffectedly mild, and decent in his whole demeanour,"[2] soon attracted attention as an authority on those scientific instruments for which the English artisans had become famous. But he became even better known as a man of

[1] Magalhães seems to have rendered his name, or had it rendered by others, variously as Jean (or John) Hyacinthe de Magalhaens, or de Magellan. Few details are known of his life, but see John Nichols, *Literary Anecdotes of the Eighteenth Century*, VIII (1814), 48–51; the articles in Michaud, *Biographie universelle;* Didot-Hoefer, *Nouvelle biographie générale;* the *Dictionary of National Biography;* and the recent sketch by J. de Carvalho in his "Correspondência científica dirigida a João Jacinto de Magalhães," *Revista da Faculdade de Ciências da Universidade de Coimbra*, 20 (1951), 93–283; reprinted separately (Coimbra, 1952).

[2] *Gentleman's Magazine*, 60 (1790), 184.

unbounded curiosity with a consuming desire to learn about—and to disseminate promptly and widely—the most recent scientific discoveries. Tireless as a letter writer, a versatile linguist with a wide European acquaintance, he kept alive an extensive and dogged correspondence. In consequence, though he published a few scientific works of modest value,[3] he was chiefly thought of in his day as a scientific intelligencer, a purveyor of scientific gossip, indeed, something of a busybody, inspiring that mixture of cautious esteem and slight exasperation we detect in some references to him.[4]

[3] His first publication was his *Description des octants et sextants Anglois . . . précédée d'un mémoire sur une nouvelle construction de ces instruments* (London, 1775). A *Description et usages des nouveaux baromètres pour mesurer la hauteur des montagnes et la profondeur des mines* (London, 1779) and a *Description of a Glass Apparatus, for Making Mineral Waters* (London, 1777, and later editions) also dealt with scientific instruments. More important was the memoir in which he gave the first extended account of the theory of latent and specific heats: *Essai sur la nouvelle théorie du feu élémentaire, et de la chaleur des corps* (London, 1780), reprinted in Rozier's *Observations sur la physique* in May and June, 1781 (17, 375–386 and 411–422), and described by Douglas McKie and Niels H. de V. Heathcote, *The Discovery of Specific and Latent Heats* (London, 1935), pp. 40–45.

[4] J. P. Brissot, who met him in London, wrote that Magellan "connaissait toutes les machines dont l'Angleterre fourmillait et, en s'occupant à les répandre par toute l'Europe, en se faisant le correspondant de tous les savants, il était parvenu . . . à une indépendance honorable" (*Mémoires*, ed. Cl. Perroud [Paris, 1911] I, 363). Brissot, who attempted in 1782–1784 to establish a center in London for the exchange of scientific information, found in Magellan a kindred spirit and remarked of him: "Il est un des premiers qui ait deviné combien la communication rapide & générale des découvertes pouvait être utile aux Sciences, & qui l'ait executé dans le centre le plus favorable pour le succès de cette correspondance,

A clubbable and inquisitive man, Magellan probably frequented Benjamin Franklin's circle of the Honest Whigs, with its strongly philosophic flavor and a scientific membership that included, besides Joseph Priestley, electrical experimenters like John Canton and William Watson; the economist, Richard Price; the merchant-naturalist, Peter Collinson; and the principal secretary of the Royal Society of London, Matthew Maty. But there is no definite evidence to link him with this group, beyond the nature of his interests, the range of his friendships, and a casual reference to him in an early letter of Franklin to Priestley (May 4, 1772).[5] Franklin, who judged men well, seems to have discerned the merit and the utility of this odd personage, for he promoted Magellan's interests in various ways and chose on occasion to communicate through him with his scientific friends abroad. Priestley, who probably met him through Franklin or at the Honest Whigs, also found Magellan useful, as we shall see, but in addition genuinely liked him, enjoyed his conversation and worldly knowledge, and spoke of him as "very friendly, especially in every thing that related to my philosophical pursuits." [6] Not everyone, however, trusted his discretion. James Watt, for example, described him to

à Londres même" (*Journal du Licée de Londres,* I [1784] 194, note 1).

[5] A. H. Smyth, ed., *Writings of Benjamin Franklin,* V, 394–396.

[6] *Memoirs of the Rev. Dr. Joseph Priestley* (London, 1809), p. 66. Priestley recalls the pleasant evenings he spent with Magellan during the famous visit to Paris in 1774 in the company of Lord Shelburne and notes the fact that Magellan accompanied him back to London. But he nowhere indicates when his association with Magellan began.

Joseph Black as "well-meaning, but no philosopher," and warned Black that "he has an extensive correspondence and may circulate erroneous doctrines to the prejudice of your honor." [7] But even Watt used his services and through him sent drawings and specifications to the French engineers who were to erect his improved steam engine in France.

At all events, Magellan's friendly assiduity and the high patronage of Priestley and Franklin made him a Fellow of the Royal Society in 1774. Ten years later, doubtless at Franklin's prompting, the American Philosophical Society elected him a Fellow. He responded by sending shipments of books and instruments and by endowing the Magellanic Prize, which has been awarded since his time to "the author of the best Discovery, or most useful Improvement relating to Navigation or Natural Philosophy." [8]

Despite these honors and credentials Magellan's chief distinction may well turn out to be the part he played in 1771–1772, at a turning point in the history of chemistry, as a *trait d'union* between the largely insulated scientific

[7] A reference to Magellan's intention of attributing the discovery of latent and specific heats, not to Black, but to the Swedish scientist, Johan Carl Wilcke. See James Patrick Muirhead, *The Origin and Progress of the Mechanical Inventions of James Watt* (London, 1854), II, 117–118. Richard Kirwan in 1788 accused Magellan of "plundering my *Mineralogy*" for his edition of Cronstedt and expressed regret to Sir Joseph Banks that he had not taken Banks's advice to beware of Magellan (Warren R. Dawson, ed., *The Banks Letters* [London, 1958], 493).

[8] *Early Proceedings of the American Philosophical Society, 1744–1838* (Philadelphia, 1884), pp. 121–122 and 135. The "Certificate Book" of the Royal Society shows that on January 20, 1774, Magellan's certificate was signed by Joseph Priestley and Benjamin Franklin. I owe this information to Professor Robert Schofield, of the Case Institute of Technology.

worlds of Britain and France. Yet this aspect of his career has not, so far as I know, been hitherto brought to light.

The earliest trace of Magellan's epistolary activity is a letter to him from the French astronomer, Charles Messier, published in the *Philosophical Transactions* in 1769. If he wrote in these early years to other scientists in France, like his friend Bory, we have no evidence of the fact. But the letters that have survived show that by 1770 Magellan was engaged in a rather special pursuit, acting as unpaid confidential agent of the French Government and regularly informing Trudaine de Montigny, who was director of the French Government's Bureau de commerce, of important British inventions and technical improvements.[9] This French program of industrial espionage, for it deserves this rather strong term, was no recent innovation; it had been carried on with great success by Trudaine de Montigny's father and predecessor in office, the much-admired Daniel Trudaine (1703–1769), who over the years had made regular use of technically trained agents to ferret out the secrets of foreign, and especially British, industrial superiority.[10] At first Magellan's role was no dif-

[9] Arthur Birembaut, "Sur les lettres du physicien Magellan conservées aux Archives Nationales," *Revue d'histoire des sciences,* 9 (1956), 150–161.

[10] A brief account of Daniel Trudaine's program of industrial espionage is given in my "French Antecedents of the Chemical Revolution," *loc. cit.,* pp. 94–98. A careful study of the Trudaines, father and son, is badly needed, but see Suzanne Delorme, "Une famille de grands Commis de l'Etat, amis des Sciences au XVIII⁰ siècle: Les Trudaine," *Revue d'histoire des sciences,* 3 (1950), 101–109. Capitaine Andrieux's *Trudaine, sa vie, son oeuvre, ses idées* (Clermont-Ferrand, 1922) is of little value, but there is useful material in Ernest Chouillier, "Les Trudaines," *Revue de Champagne et de Brie,* 14 (1883), 19–20 and 131–138.

ferent from that of such other agents as Gabriel Jars, J. P. F. Guillot Duhamel, John Holker, and Nicolas Desmarest, for we find him sending the younger Trudaine packages of books and pamphlets describing new inventions and even, on one occasion, attempting to smuggle out of England a new kind of loom the British were reluctant to export.

Magellan's interests were, however, primarily scientific, and we soon find him reporting on the new instruments of John Bird (1709–1776), Jesse Ramsden (1735–1800), and other skilled English artisans and sending samples of British flint glass so that French astronomers could equip themselves with achromatic refractors like those which John Dollond had successfully made some years before. This could not have displeased Trudaine de Montigny, who, though a far less able administrator than his father, was more scientifically inclined. Succeeding to his father's place in the Academy of Sciences in 1764, the younger Trudaine displayed a keener interest in its affairs than had his father; was on terms of intimacy with a number of the scientists; and later became—as is well known—a friend, patron, disciple, and (for a brief time and to a modest extent) the collaborator of Lavoisier.[11] It was at Trudaine's instigation and as a reward for his services to the Bureau de commerce that Magellan on September 4, 1771, was made a corresponding member of the Academy, assigned to keep in touch with his old friend Bory.[12] Yet even before this formal association with the Academy, Magellan was writing with some regularity to its distin-

[11] Ralph E. Oesper, "Priestley, Lavoisier, and Trudaine de Montigny," *Journal of Chemical Education*, 13 (1936), 403–412.
[12] Birembaut, *loc. cit.*, p. 156.

guished senior chemist, P. J. Macquer. Some of this correspondence, or at least of Magellan's part of it, has survived to tell a surprising story: that it was, in a manner of speaking, as a by-product of the French program of industrial and technical espionage, carried on by the two Trudaines, that a knowledge of British progress in pneumatic chemistry was at last brought to the attention of the French scientists.

The Introduction of Pneumatic Chemistry into France

On May 4, 1771, Magellan dispatched to Macquer from London the first letter that has been preserved from this correspondence. In this letter he recalls his promise, made during a visit to Paris the summer before, to send Macquer specimens of "gomme élastique," by which he means, of course, crude rubber.[13] For some years Macquer had been investigating the properties of this novel material, this barbarously named *caoutchouc*, which La Condamine had first brought to the attention of the scientific world; [14] in fact, Macquer had already published, in two memoirs, the first serious studies of rubber in chemical literature.[15]

[13] Macquer correspondence, Bibliothèque Nationale, Paris, MS Fr. 12306, no. 11.

[14] "Mémoire sur une résine élastique, nouvellement découverte à Cayenne par M. Fresneau," *Mém. Acad. roy. sci.* for 1751 (1755), pp. 319–333. La Condamine had sent samples of rubber from Peru as early as 1736, soon after his arrival at Quito on the famous geodetic expedition.

[15] For Macquer's research on rubber see Coleby, *op. cit.*, pp. 116–117. An unpublished letter of Bertin to Macquer, dated Versailles, April 21, 1768, shows that the government, or at least this enlightened minister, took more than a casual interest in Macquer's research. Bertin thanks Macquer for sending him a copy of the memoir

Magellan's letter goes on to explain that he had long since asked a friend in Portugal to obtain samples for him but that these had only recently been received and would be forwarded. Then, changing the subject, he remarks that Macquer must surely know that an English translation of his famous *Dictionnaire de chymie* had recently been announced in London. According to the prospectus, which Magellan has seen, the English edition is to be accompanied by notes of the translator.

This was news to Macquer, who apparently wrote asking Magellan to send more information; for when the latter replied on August 20, he announced that he had already purchased from the bookseller twenty-five gatherings of the forthcoming book and would pack them, specially marked, in a box destined for Trudaine de Montigny, so that Trudaine's secretary could transmit them to the chemist.[16] He had not been able to identify the translator, Magellan wrote, except that he is "un gentil-home [*sic*] de Birmingham & qu'il fait travailler des mines de fer pour son compte"; though primarily a metallurgist, as some of his notes indicate, he is not ignorant of chemistry. Magellan then quoted a significant passage from the prospectus. Such a project as the *Dictionnaire,* so ran the comments of the translator, was perhaps too vast for one man to carry out, and the author has left out many articles which should have been included. The chief omissions are due

---

on "la résine élastique," and continues: "Je me felicite vrayment de vous avoir engagé à travailler a un objet dont on peut tirer avantage, d'après la bonne découverte que vous avés fait. Mandés moy je vous prie si M. de Vaucanson en a connoissance" (Bib. Nat., MS Fr. 12305, no. 113).

16 Bib. Nat., MS Fr. 12306, no. 13.

to "the Author not having been acquainted with some very late discoveries, specialy [*sic*] those important ones Concerning *fixable air,* made by Doctor Black, Professor of Chemistry in the University of Edinburgh, by Doct. Macbride (of Dublin), and by the Honorable Mr. Cavendish." [17] These omissions he proposes to remedy by adding notes of his own.

Of Macquer and his *Dictionnaire,* which indeed suffers from these significant omissions, little need be said, for the man and the book are, or should be, familiar to all students of the history of chemistry. Though only an *associé chimiste* of the Academy of Sciences at the age of fifty-three, Macquer unquestionably ranked as France's outstanding chemist. The author of some twenty memoirs and of one of the best textbooks to appear during the century, he taught chemistry in public lectures at the Jardin du Roi. In 1766 he succeeded to two technical governmental posts: that of Inspector General of the dye industry and that of chief scientist of the porcelain factory at Sèvres. The same year he published anonymously in two volumes his *Dictionnaire de chymie,* a remarkably successful work, which he hastened to acknowledge in later editions and which was translated into English, Ger-

[17] *Ibid.,* no. 13. An almost identical comment appears in the preface to the translation. See *A Dictionary of Chemistry* (London, 1777), I, pp. iii and iv. For convenience I have worked from this second English printing, but I was able to compare it with the first English edition of 1771 in the Library of the Institute of the History of Medicine of the Johns Hopkins University. An important note concerning factitious airs discusses the work of Hales, Cotes, Black, and Cavendish (I, 33, note b). Macquer's article on quicklime is translated intact; but in a long note (I, 602, note 1), Black's theory of causticity is carefully explained.

man, Italian, and Danish. No single work, I believe, can give the modern student a better picture of the state of Continental chemistry before Lavoisier than this first edition of Macquer's dictionary.

Less eminent, though destined to be a figure of note, was the man who undertook the first English translation of Macquer's two volumes and whose name Magellan did not at first know. James Keir (1735–1820), the "gentleman of Birmingham," had studied medicine at Edinburgh in company with the famous Erasmus Darwin.[18] Unlike his lifelong friend, he did not enter medical practice but served instead with the army in the West Indies until after the close of the Seven Years' War. On his return to England he settled at Birmingham about 1770, probably at the urging of Darwin and Matthew Boulton, and devoted himself to the study of chemistry. Perhaps, as Magellan suggests, he launched his career of industrial chemist as a mineowner and metallurgist. Later, however, we find him the coproprietor of a glassworks at nearby Stourbridge; and in 1778 he abandoned this venture to take over, for a time, the direction of Boulton's Soho works. In 1780, in partnership with an old army friend, Alexander Blair, he founded a chemical factory at Tipton to exploit a process he had developed for the manufacture of alkali. Never far removed from Birmingham, he was one of the

[18] Mrs. Amelia Moilliet's privately printed *Sketch of the Life of J. Keir, F.R.S.* (London, 1859) is the chief biographical source; the main facts are summarized in the *Dictionary of National Biography*. Keir's relations to Darwin and others of the Lunar Society are set forth in Hesketh Pearson, *Doctor Darwin* (London and Toronto, 1930). His position as a pioneer industrial chemist is emphasized in Archibald and Nan L. Clow, *The Chemical Revolution* (London, 1952), pp. 95–100, 133, and *passim*.

honored members, and indeed one of the founders, of the Lunar Society, the extraordinary group of midland worthies that included Darwin, Boulton, James Watt, Josiah Wedgwood, and, after 1780, Joseph Priestley. Keir's chemical investigations were always industrially oriented: he worked on new alloys with Boulton; he studied the crystallization observed in glass and experimented with glazes for Wedgwood's pottery; but he also kept alive a keen interest in pneumatic chemistry, remained a staunch phlogistonist, as Humphry Davy later testified, and discussed problems with Priestley and performed difficult analyses for him. A number of Keir's papers were published in the *Philosophical Transactions*. He became a Fellow of the Royal Society in 1785.

It was perhaps to refurbish the chemistry he had learned at Edinburgh as a student of Andrew Plummer that Keir undertook, soon after resigning his army commission, to render Macquer's *Dictionnaire* into English. The task, as we have seen, was completed by 1771. Early in October the last two gatherings had come off the press, and the alert Magellan sent them on to Macquer in Paris.[19] Later in the same month our intelligencer raised once again the problem of "fixed air," for he had recently had, he wrote, a conversation with a friend who had supplied information which perhaps "n'est pas connu en France de tous les curieux."[20] This information, chiefly the names of works written on this absorbing topic, he forthwith reported to Macquer. Seemingly unaware that Meyer's work had been translated into French, he refers in this let-

[19] Letter dated London, October 5, 1771 (Bib. Nat., MS Fr. 12306, no. 15).
[20] Letter dated October 25, 1771 (*ibid.*, no. 16).

47

ter to the German apothecary's treatise on lime, with
its theory of *acidum pingue*, remarking that "le Dr.
Black d'Edinburgh tache d'expliquer les memes phenomenes
par son systeme de l'*air fixe* ou *fixable*." A certain Mr. Rousseau of Munich, he continues, has made quicklime with the
solar heat of a burning glass and finds that it will not
yield the *lapis infernalis*. This experiment, "bien digne
d'etre repetée et bien examinée par un homme Comme
Vous," seems to prove that ordinary fire, in driving out
from calcareous stones some particles of water and
fixed air, deposits some of its particles, or a certain
phlogistic and inflammable principle.[21]

Magellan then informed Macquer about two other German works dealing with "fixed air": Nicolas Jacquin's
Examen chemicum [22] and a pamphlet by a certain "M^r.
Crantz," entitled *Examinis chemici doctrinae Meyerianae
. . . rectificatio*,[23] which had appeared in 1770. And Magellan added:

[21] If these results were actually printed, I have not identfied the
work in which they appear. This chemist was probably Georg Lud-
wig Claudius Rousseau (1724–1794), who is accorded an article by
Poggendorff, but is not mentioned by Kopp or Hoefer. There are
several references to Rousseau in J. F. Gmelin, *Geschichte der
Chemie* (Göttingen, 1797–1799). See especially II, 713 and III,
475. Rousseau was an apothecary of Ingolstadt (not Munich) and
professor at that Bavarian university.

[22] Nicolaus Joseph von Jacquin, *Examen chemicum doctrinae
Meyerianae de acido pingui et Blackianae de aere fixo, respectu
calcis* (Vienna, 1769). This book of N. J. Jacquin (1727–1817), a
professor of botany and chemistry at Vienna, was translated into
German in 1770; its first effect was to launch in Germany and Holland a controversy on the relative merits of the ideas of Black—
which Jacquin defended—and those of Meyer. For Jacquin see
Hoefer, *op. cit.*, II, 335–336, and John Ferguson, *Bibliotheca
chemica* (Glasgow, 1906), I, 432.

[23] Heinrich Johann Nepomuk von Crantz (1722–1799); the full

Je puis vous envoyer Ces deux brochures d'ici, en cas que Vous ne les ayez pas à Paris. Je souhaite que vous examinies bien cette matierre, & ce qu'on a ecrit sur elle. Vous saves que Macbride en a traité & dans les Transact. Philosoph. dernierement (il y a environ 3 ou 4 annees) il y a des bonnes experiences sur celà par M^r. Cavandish [sic] & une [sic] Memoire de M^r. Lane, qui a fait des eaux calybeates par le moien de l'air fixe.[24]

Here we find assembled for Macquer's enlightenment the names and works of several of those men Lavoisier was later to discuss with such care in the historical section of his *Opuscules physiques et chymiques* (1774).[25] But it is likely that Lavoisier at this time was just as ignorant of them as Macquer probably was. Macquer, for his part, seems to have paid little attention to Magel-

---

title of the work cited is *Examinis chemici doctrinae Meyerianae de acido pingui et Blackianae de aëre fixo respectu calcis rectificatio* (Leipzig, 1770). It is a defense of Meyer. For Crantz see the *Allgemeine Deutsche Biographie*. He is not mentioned in Poggendorff.

[24] Lane, a London apothecary, whom Priestley was to cite with approval, published a paper describing how iron could be dissolved by water impregnated with "fixed air." See *Philosophical Transactions*, 59 (1769), 216–227.

[25] *Oeuvres de Lavoisier*, I, 480–498. Among the works stimulated by the controversy of Meyer and Jacquin we may cite Johann Jacob Well's *Rechtfertigung der Black'schen Lehre von der fixirten Luft* (Vienna, 1771), Christian Ehrenfried Weigel's *Observationes chemicae et mineralogicae* (Göttingen, 1771), J. R. Spielmann's *Examen acidi pinguis* (Strasbourg, 1769). Wilhelm Bucholz' *Chemische Versuche über das Meyerische Acidum Pingue* (Weimer, 1771) was reviewed in the *Journal encyclopédique* (August 15, 1772, pp. 72–77). I doubt whether Macquer or Lavoisier was familiar with any of these works. In his *Opuscules* Lavoisier mentions Weigel's work but remarks, "Il ne m'a pas encore été possible de me procurer cet ouvrage" (*Oeuvres*, I, 555).

lan's revelations; it was necessary to renew the attack at a later date.

Magellan, Joseph Priestley, and the French Chemists

One name is notably absent from the list of authors Magellan transmitted to Macquer on October 25, 1771— the name of Joseph Priestley. This, of course, is understandable. At this time Priestley had not gone far with his experiments on gases and had yet to publish any of his results.[26] It was not until March, 1772, that Priestley, at a series of meetings of the Royal Society, first made public the experiments which were to form the major part of his "Observations on Different Kinds of Air." [27] This important classic, it should bear repeating, was not published until late in 1772, after Lavoisier had carried out his first experiments on combustion.

But did Magellan know Priestley as early as 1771? Could it have been Priestley who first told Magellan of Keir's translation and of the criticism leveled against Macquer's book? Was Priestley, perhaps, "the friend" who told Magellan about the writings of Meyer, Jacquin,

[26] W. Cameron Walker's earlier paper ("The Beginnings of the Scientific Career of Joseph Priestley," *Isis*, 21 [1934], 81–97) has been largely superseded by Robert E. Schofield's "Scientific Background of Joseph Priestley," *Annals of Science*, 13, no. 3 (1957; published April, 1959), 148–163. Priestley's interest in gases began before he settled at Leeds in September, 1767, and found his plentiful supply of "fixed air" from the nearby public brewery. Between the fall of 1767 and the end of 1768 he was occupied with the production of artificial Pyrmont water. His more important discoveries were made in the course of 1771–1772.

[27] See my "Joseph Priestley's First Papers on Gases," *loc. cit.*, pp. 1–7.

and Crantz? Likely as this seemed to me, there appeared at first to be no positive evidence that the two men were acquainted at this early date. A suggestive clue, however, was supplied by Priestley's *History of Vision, Light, and Colours* published in 1772. Appended to this book is a list of those works "of which Dr. Priestley is already possessed, or to which he has access, for compiling The History of Experimental Philosophy." [28] A number of chemical writings are included, and among these one finds listed the French translation of Meyer and, rather surprisingly, the pamphlets of Jacquin and Crantz. Exceedingly rare today, the last two works could not have been common even then. Only a man with Priestley's special interests would have been likely to seek them out: he is the most promising candidate for the role of Magellan's "friend." But were these men acquainted, as we know them to have been a year later? The answer is supplied by the manuscript Journal Book of the Royal Society, where it is recorded that on March 14, 1771, Magellan attended a meeting of the Society as Priestley's guest. There is supporting testimony from Priestley himself. In a letter to the Dutch scientist, Ingenhousz, written ten years later, Priestley recalled that when he was making his experiments on the behavior of plants in vitiated air— experiments carried out in 1771 and 1772—he "wrote to my friends about them, particularly Mr. Magellan, and desired him to communicate my observations to you, as well as to others." [29] I think it highly probable, therefore,

[28] Joseph Priestley, *The History and Present State of Discoveries Relating to Vision, Light, and Colours* (London, 1772). The list of books is not paginated.

[29] The quotation from this letter of November 21, 1781, and the

that the first information the French chemists received about the state of pneumatic chemistry abroad can be traced in the first instance to Joseph Priestley.

It was Magellan, at all events, who informed the French scientific world, in the spring of 1772, about the important discoveries Priestley had reported during the month of March at meetings of the Royal Society. This he apparently did, if we accept the evidence of the letter to Ingenhousz, with Priestley's approval, if not at his urging.

Priestley, to be sure, was already known in France for his *History and Present State of Electricity*, which had appeared in a French translation in 1771.[30] Here, in a chapter on the conduction of electricity in "mephitic air," his name for carbon dioxide, Priestley mentions in passing that he had carried out experiments which convinced him that mephitic air was a fluid quite different from common air. This brief reference to his chemical work on gases, though the first he allowed to appear in print, could hardly have attracted the attention of French chemists. The information that he had been seriously investigating fixed air and other elastic fluids seems to have been first imparted by letters that Magellan wrote to Macquer in March, 1772.

---

entry in the manuscript "Journal Book of the Royal Society," vol. XVII (1771–1774), 45, were communicated to me by Professor Schofield, who is preparing a detailed study of Priestley.

[30] First published in 1767, and again in 1770, it had been translated into French by a disciple of the Abbé Nollet, with the addition of anti-Franklinist footnotes, as *Histoire de l'électricité, traduite de l'Anglois de Joseph Priestley, avec des notes critiques* (3 vols.; Paris, 1771). For the passage on mephitic air see this translation, especially III, 212–213. There is no reference to this passage in the review that appeared in the December, 1771, issue of Rozier's journal (*Introduction aux observations*, I, 389–394).

The first we have is dated March 20, 1772; from it I cite the following important paragraph:

On Continua hier à Lire l'excellent Memoire sur l'air fixe & le Mephitique, par M^r. Priestley, dans La Soc^e Royale & on y a lu aussi la Communication d'un Medecin ou Chirurgien qui Cura d'une terrible fievre putride un malade en Lui appliquant par L'anus l'air fixe, qui se degageoit de la mixture de l'acide vitriolique avec le *chalk* ou pierre à *Chaux* moienant un tube qui étoit adapté à un Verre où ledite mixture [*sic*] ou solution se faisoit.[31]

It is clearly implied that Magellan had previously reported to Macquer the earlier readings of Priestley's memoir to the Royal Society on March 5 and 12, but no such letter appears to have survived. Echoes of its contents, however, have come down to us. At the session of the Academy of Sciences held on April 1, 1772, Macquer read a letter of Magellan containing two of Priestley's observations: on the restoration of vitiated air by the gaseous exchange of plants and on the curative power of "fixed air" taken rectally.[32] This letter was evidently passed on to the Abbé Rozier, who published a short notice of Priestley's discoveries in the April issue of his journal, the *Observations sur la physique.* Since this notice appeared under the heading "Nouvelles littéraries," it was not reproduced in the quarto reprint of 1777 and has only recently been brought to light by Douglas McKie in a careful study of the rare duodecimo edition of the *Ob-*

[31] Bib. Nat., MS Fr. 12306, no. 18. The enterprising surgeon was Mr. William Hey, a friend whose work Priestley was to cite in his first published work on gases.

[32] *Procès-verbaux*, 91 (1772), under date of April 1, 1772.

servations. It is worth reproducing here as the first significant printed reference in France to Priestley's work on air:

Monsieur Priestly, connu par une histoire de l'électricité,
dont nous avons rendu compte, dans le Volume de Décembre
1771, page 36, a lu à la Société Royale de Londres, un Mémoire
intéressant, dont nous nous empressons de faire connoitre le
sujet; il est intitulé: *Recherches sur la nature de l'air & des
parties qui le composent.* Cet ouvrage est fondé sur un grand
nombre d'expériences curieuses, & M. Priestly y développe
comment la nature supplée à cette prodigieuse quantité d'air
consumé ou détruit par le feu & par la flamme, & il prouve par
des expériences, que la végétation des plantes contribue à le
remplacer & à lui faire reprendre ses qualités; que l'air vicié
& infecté par les vapeurs qui s'exhalent des corps tendans à la
corruption & dêja corrumpus, peut être renouvellé & réparé
par l'air fixe qui s'échappe d'un corps en fermentation.

On a donné à un malade un lavement d'air fixe, produit par
une combinaison d'acide vitriolique & de terre calcaire, & ce
remede singulier l'a heureusement délivré d'une fievre maligne
& putride, qui avoit résisté à tous les antiseptiques connus. Ce
remede a été hasardé par un Chirurgien de la petite ville de
Léeds.[33]

From the attention paid to Priestley's work on plants,
which is not mentioned in the earliest surviving letter, it
is clear that these important observations were reported
in an earlier letter of Magellan missing from the correspondence, perhaps because Rozier, who based his account on it, never returned it.

[33] McKie, "The 'Observations' of the Abbé François Rozier," *loc.
cit.,* pp. 85–86. Professor McKie writes: "It will be seen that there
was reliable detailed news of [Priestley's work on air] in Paris in
April 1772, a month after it was read in London." He appears to be
unaware of Magellan's role.

A curious fact may be mentioned in passing: Lavoisier was present at the meeting where the letter concerning Priestley's work was read but does not seem to have been particularly struck by what he heard. Surviving among Lavoisier's papers are minutes in his hand, a so-called *plumitif*, which he took down for his own purposes during the meetings he attended during most of 1772. This document differs at numerous points from the official minutes of the Secretary, chiefly by emphasizing matters which attracted Lavoisier especially. Under the date of April 1 he has nothing to say about the news of Priestley's work. The subject seems not to have interested him.

Nevertheless, it was not these inadequate reports on Priestley's great discoveries, but Priestley's first publication on gases, his *Directions for Impregnating Water with Fixed Air,* a portion of his research published separately in June, 1772, which first attracted real attention in France.[34] Somewhat surprisingly, it took this pamphlet on making artificial Seltzer water, or Pyrmont water, as the English called it—to our modern eyes a rather trivial affair and much less significant than the work of Black or even MacBride—to awaken French scientists, after their long slumber, to the possibilities of pneumatic chemistry.[35]

[34] Professor McKie seems to exaggerate when he writes that there was reliable and detailed news in Paris of Priestley's work a month after it was read in London. And I do not believe that it was these reports that led Lavoisier to include Priestley's name in the list of pneumatic chemists given in his famous memorandum of February, 1773, where, incidentally, he does not mention "Priestley's experiments on air," but merely lists his name.

[35] Joseph Priestley, LL.D. F.R.S., *Directions for Impregnating Water with Fixed Air; In order to communicate to it the peculiar Spirit and Virtues of Pyrmont Water, and other Mineral Waters of a similar Nature* (London: Printed for J. Johnson, No. 72, in St. Paul's Church-Yard, 1772). A facsimile of this pamphlet was printed

The presumed medical value of this little pamphlet chiefly accounts for the excitement it aroused and the surprising attention bestowed upon it. In twenty-two pages Priestley describes a simple method of saturating water with Black's "fixed air," generated by the action of dilute sulphuric acid on chalk, and advocates the use of the impregnated water to cure scurvy, putrid fevers, and such maladies as diseased lungs, ulcerous sore throat, and even cancers. In the author's opinion, he was only making more accessible and easier to administer the new therapeutic substance, "fixed air," whose virtues had been demonstrated by Dr. MacBride, Sir John Pringle, Dr. Brownrigg,[36] and others. Probably it was the supposed efficacy of "fixed air" in the cure of scurvy, a pressing medical problem of immediate importance to maritime nations, which particularly commended Priestley's book to the Lord Commissioners of the Admiralty, to his friend Benjamin Franklin, always on the lookout for discoveries of practical import, and to French officials like Trudaine de Montigny, when they came to hear of it. Yet for our purposes what is important is that it seems to have been this modest book which at last focused attention in France on the neglected subject of Black's "fixed air."

It was Magellan, of course, who made Priestley's little

---

in Washington, D.C., in 1945 by the American Bottlers of Carbonated Beverages.

[36] For William Brownrigg, who reported that Pyrmont and similar mineral waters owe their acidulous taste to the presence of fixed air, see J. Russell-Wood, "A Biographical Note on William Brownrigg, M.D., F.R.S. (1711–1800)," *Annals of Science*, 6 (1949), 186–196, and the same author's "The Scientific Work of William Brownrigg," *loc. cit.*, 6 (1949), 436–447, and 7 (1951), 77–94 and 199–206.

book known in Paris. On July 5 he sent to an unidentified correspondent a summary of recent work on the presumed curative power of "fixed air"; in this account he referred briefly to the work of Pringle, MacBride, Brownrigg, Lane, and Joseph Black and then presented an extended summary in his awkward French of Priestley's method of making soda water, with some slight modifications based on his own experiments.[37] Two days later he wrote to Trudaine de Montigny, enclosing a copy of this correspondence, with the information that he had dispatched copies of Priestley's pamphlet by the last post. Magellan suggested that the Intendant of Finance might have his summary printed, after the French had been corrected, as a broadside to be widely distributed.[38]

It was at this point—a month before he wrote his August memorandum—that Lavoisier entered the picture, though not as significantly as one might have expected. Trudaine, who was then at his château at Montigny, wrote Lavoisier on July 14, 1772, the following interesting letter, which is worth reproducing in full. With it he enclosed Magellan's communication of July 7, as well as a copy of the Priestley pamphlet.

M. De Lavoisier fermier general

A Montigny ce 14 Juillet 1772

J'ay l'honneur de vous envoyer, Monsieur, une lettre que je recois de M. Magallhaens Anglois catholique correspondant

[37] *Oeuvres de Lavoisier—Correspondance recueillie et annotée par René Fric* (Fascicule II, 1770–1775), (Paris, 1957), pp. 356–366. M. Fric believes the unknown recipient of this document to have been Trudaine de Montigny. But the original letter was probably written to Rozier, with a copy sent to Trudaine.

[38] *Ibid.*, pp. 366–367.

de l'academie, au sujet d'une decouverte tres importante Sur l'air fixe. j'y joins la petite brochure de M. Priestley qui est parfaitement bien faite a ce qu'il m'a paru. j'imagine que vous entendez bien l'anglois. vous feriez une très bonne oeuvre très utile de faire publier cet ouvrage traduit avec les notes de M. Magallhaens. je vous prie aussi de vouloir bien repeter ces experiences, et d'ajouter vos propres observations. je vais repetter moi même ces experiences. en consequence, je vous prie de me renvoyer ma petite brochure aussitôt que vous l'aurez traduite ou fait traduire ce qui ne peut être long. le merite de ces nouvelles decouvertes etant la promptitude j'espere que vous ne tarderez pas a faire paroistre ce petit ouvrage. il n'y aura pas de mal a en prendre un nombre d'exemplaires pour faire distribuer gratis, principalement aux medecins. dans le desir de donner satisfaction à M. Magallhaens j'ay cru ne pouvoir mieux m'adresser qu'a vous je Scais votre exactitude Sur les details de Phisique et de Chimie et je Scais que c'est vous obliger que de vous mettre a portée de faire une chose utile. je travaille actuellement a devenir votre confrere chimiste. j'ay un laboratoire dont je ne Sors pas depuis trois jours qu'il est fini. Si je Suivois mon gout je m'y livrerois davantage. mais vous qui êtes jeune et qui avez du tems a vous, je vous exhorte a l'employer aussi utilement. vous connoissez depuis longtems, Monsieur, mon estime pour vos talens, et pour votre personne, et les Sentimens avec lesquels j'ay l'honneur d'être bien Sincerement, je vous assure, Monsieur, Votre très humble et très obeïssant serviteur.

TRUDAINE [39]

There is no evidence that Lavoisier followed Trudaine's exhortation and repeated—at least at this time—Priestley's simple experiments on soda water, though he was sufficiently interested to read Magellan's letter to the Academy

[39] *Ibid.*, pp. 368–369.

at its meeting of July 18.[40] He could not very well have responded to Trudaine's suggestion that he translate Priestley's pamphlet into French, for his English, if he had any at all, would have been inadequate to the task. Probably he did not even instigate the translation, for when the French version, apparently the work of Rozier himself, did appear, not long after, it is Trudaine de Montigny who is credited with making it available to the French reader.[41] Although we do not have Lavoisier's reply to Trudaine's letter, it is at least possible that he reminded Trudaine that Rozier was in a good position to have Priestley's work translated afresh or to have Magellan's summary corrected.

Lavoisier was already on familiar terms with Rozier, who in succeeding months was to play a central part in spreading abroad through the pages of his recently founded journal a knowledge of English pneumatic chemistry, giving generous space to abridgments and translations of the work of the British chemists and their Continental supporters and critics. For this important contribution Rozier deserves more attention than he has received.

A native of the Lyonnais who had won a modest reputation as an agronomist and man of science, François Rozier (1734–1793) was probably best known, before his arrival in Paris, for a prize-winning essay on the chemistry of winemaking.[42] For a short time he had been director of

[40] *Procès-verbaux*, 91 (1772), fol. 254 verso, where we read: "M. Lavoisier a lu une lettre de M. Magellens au sujet de L'air fixe."

[41] When, on August 14, Trudaine distributed at the Academy of Sciences copies of the translation of Priestley's brochure, it was described as translated "de L'Anglois de M. Joseph Priestley par M. L. Rozier" (*Procès-verbaux*, 91, fol. 286 verso).

[42] For Rozier, besides the articles in the *Nouvelle biographie gé-*

the Ecole royale de médecine vétérinaire, established at Lyons in 1763 by the eminent Bourgelat. Deprived of his post after a dispute with the founder, Rozier retired to his father's estate near Lyons and for a time devoted himself to agricultural experiments, living on a small inheritance, which the cost of those experiments soon dissipated. About 1771, having been made Chevalier de l'Eglise de Lyon, a minor decoration which brought with it a modest competence, he moved to Paris and acquired the rights to a defunct scientific publication, the *Observations sur l'histoire naturelle, sur la physique et sur la peinture,* which had appeared, with variations of title but without notable success, between 1752 and 1758. Under Rozier's energetic editorship the first issue of a wholly reconstituted journal appeared in July, 1771, with the title *Observations sur la physique, sur l'histoire naturelle et sur les arts.*[43]

nérale and in Quérard, *La France littéraire,* the reader may consult A. J. Dugour, "Notice sur la vie et les écrits de l'Abbé Rozier," in Rozier's posthumous *Cours complet d'agriculture . . . ou dictionnaire universel d'agriculture,* X (An VIII–1800), pp. i–xvi; Alphonse de Boisseau, *Eloge de l'Abbé Rozier* (Lyon, 1832); and the sketch by M. Cochard (who had married Rozier's niece), *Notice historique sur l'Abbé Rozier* (Lyon, 1832). There are glimpses of Rozier later in his career in Arthur Young's *Travels.* See Henri Sée's excellently annotated translation, *Voyages en France en 1787, 1788, et 1789,* (Paris, 1931) I, 128–130 and 452–453.

Rozier compiled a valuable index to the serial publications of the Academy of Sciences from 1666 to 1770. In his introduction he proposed a card file for compiling indexes and for similar purposes, using the blank side of ordinary playing cards. See his *Nouvelle table des articles contenus dans les volumes de l'Académie Royale des Sciences de Paris, depuis 1666 jusqu'en 1770* (Paris, 1775–1776), I, pp. xi–xii. Just such a card index, using playing cards, is to be found with the Bordeaux MS of Rouelle's chemical lectures, a MS written after 1772–1773.

[43] For Rozier's journal see, besides Douglas McKie's more recent

Rozier's new publication filled a lamentable gap in the scientific periodical literature of France, which had been largely monopolized by the leisurely publications of the Academy of Sciences. The *Observations*, by contrast, offered prompt printing of scientific results, especially in rapidly growing fields like chemistry and experimental physics; it could provide a forum for those who were not privileged to use the sacrosanct pages of the Academy's *Mémoires* or the intermittent *Savants étrangers;* above all, the editor promised to report at length on foreign books and to print translations of foreign memoirs. Not only, as Rozier pointed out to his readers, had matters reached a point where the Academic publications were no longer adequate, but there was insufficient comprehension in France of the work of foreign investigators: "Il semble qu'à mesure que le nombre des Savans s'est accru, la Correspondance, entre ceux des Nations différentes, a été rallentie." [44]

By the summer of 1772 Rozier's journal had been appearing for only a year, but it had already won wide esteem and in large measure was fulfilling its founder's objectives. In the first issues Rozier included papers by obscure but earnest contributors from the French provinces, as well as

article in *Annals of Science*, cited above, his paper "The Scientific Periodical from 1665 to 1798," in *Natural Philosophy through the Eighteenth Century and Allied Topics* (a commemoration number of the *Philosophical Magazine;* London, 1948), pp. 127–130. Some interesting material is found in E. W. J. Neave's rather disappointing "Chemistry in Rozier's Journal," *Annals of Science*, 6 (1950), 416–421; 7 (1951), 101–106, 284–299, 393–400; and 8 (1952), 28–45.

[44] Cited from Rozier's "Avis" to the reader, in the first quarto number (January, 1773), by McKie, "The Scientific Periodical," *loc. cit.*, pp. 127–129.

translations of memoirs and communications by scientists of Germany, Sweden, Switzerland, Italy, and Great Britain. Members of the Academy of Sciences were slow to take advantage of this new medium of publication, with one significant exception. Lavoisier—young, energetic, ambitious, and impatient to see his results printed as rapidly as possible—was the first academician to make extensive use of the facilities Rozier offered. In the second number (August, 1771) there appeared a summary of Lavoisier's classic experiments on the presumed transmutation of water into earth, which the young chemist had read to the Academy the previous November.[45] In the issue for May, 1772, Rozier printed Lavoisier's anonymous report on

[45] *Introduction aux observations,* I, 78–83. This purports to be an account, prepared from memory, of Lavoisier's presentation at the *séance publique* of the Academy on November 14, 1770. But Meldrum—the first to realize the importance of Rozier's journal in establishing the chronological development of Lavoisier's early work —was convinced that this summary, or material for it, had been supplied by Lavoisier himself. See Meldrum, "Lavoisier's Early Work in Science," *loc. cit.,* 20, 405–409; cf. Duveen and Klickstein, *op. cit.,* pp. 19–21.

Lavoisier's work on water had been referred to earlier in the issue of July, 1771, in an editor's footnote to the dissertation by a Swedish scientist on whether the waters of the ocean progressively diminish. See *Introduction aux observations,* I, 7. McKie has recently found in the duodecimo edition an announcement concerning the plan for the mineralogical atlas, in the course of which Rozier wrote that "Messieurs *Guettard, Lavoisier* & plusieurs Sçavans n'épargnent ni soins, ni tems, ni voyages pour perfectionner cet Atlas minéralogique." Because this notice appeared under "Nouvelles littéraires," it was not reprinted in the *Introduction aux observations* of 1777. See McKie, "The '*Observations*' of the Abbé François Rozier," *loc. cit.,* pp. 84–85. This would seem to provide additional evidence for an early and close connection between the Abbé Rozier and Lavoisier.

the experiments he had conducted with Macquer and Cadet on the destruction of the diamond.[46] In June of 1772 Lavoisier published an indignant letter to the editor concerning the "jeune homme prétendu Hydroscope," a dowser who claimed to be able to locate subterranean waters.[47] In July the journal carried an Academy report on the Abbé Bachelay's meteorite, signed by Fougeroux, Cadet, and Lavoisier; accompanying it in the same issue was Lavoisier's first printed contribution to meteorology, his "Observations sur un effet singulier du Tonnerre." [48]

There has naturally been a temptation to see Lavoisier's hand in Rozier's program—begun with the publication of a French version of Priestley's *Directions*—of disseminating the facts about British pneumatic chemistry during the course of 1772–1773. Yet I doubt if Lavoisier "took the initiative," as Meldrum suggests, in proposing the series of translations to Rozier.[49] Trudaine and Magellan are as

[46] *Introduction aux observations,* II, 108–111. See below, pp. 84–86.   [47] *Ibid.,* II, 231–232.

[48] *Ibid.,* II, 251–255 and 310–312. The issue of August, 1772, contained a letter of Lavoisier to the editor describing the project for a mineralogical atlas and asking for collaborators; this is accompanied by instructions for making useful observations (*ibid.,* II, 372–376).

[49] Meldrum has written: "I make the supposition that Lavoisier took the initiative in proposing these [translations and abridgments] to Rozier, who was the editor, and that Rozier concurred, willing to let matter of moment and controversy appear in his periodical. It is certain that Lavoisier took a far greater interest in gases than any other French chemist" (*Eighteenth Century Revolution in Science,* p. 28). This, of course, is only speculation. That contemporaries associated Lavoisier with these translations and abridgments is, however, suggested by the following passage written in 1774: "M. de Lavoisier, de notre Académie des sciences, vient de traduire et de rassembler en un volume in-8° tout ce qui a été écrit et s'est dit

likely instigators, if, perhaps, we should not give the principal credit to Rozier himself; these men were already in close communication, and there is evidence that Rozier was already using material transmitted to him by Trudaine from Magellan.[50] So close, indeed, was the relationship of Trudaine and Rozier, that the latter was in the habit, at least he was some years later, of receiving packages of books and other items by using Trudaine's address and franking privilege; [51] this (as we have seen) was already

---

depuis deux ans *sur la découverte de l'air fixe*. Quoiqu'il n'y ait rien de lui dans ce recueil, la manière dont il a redigé les différents ouvrages qui ont paru en Angleterre sur ces objet mérite des éloges, et son travail a un grand succès. Ce sont principalement les *Mémoires* de M. Priestley, Anel [*sic*], Macbride, qu'il nous a transmis. On dit cet ouvrage très-curieux et très intéressant" (*Correspondance littéraire, philosophique et critique par Grimm, Diderot, Raynal, Meister, etc.*, ed. Maurice Tourneux [Paris, 1879], X, 349). No such work by Lavoisier is known; indeed, this is certainly a woefully inaccurate reference, at second hand, to Lavoisier's *Opuscules physiques et chimiques*, which appeared in January, 1774. This, of course, included a long historical section making full use of the translations printed by Rozier; but original work by Lavoisier is very definitely included. The passage hardly deserves notice, except as it may reflect contemporary rumor that Lavoisier had something to do with the translations that had appeared; this evidence is far from weighty.

[50] The "Description du barometre de Ramsden," which Rozier printed in January, 1772 (*Introduction aux observations*, I, 509–512), suggests to me a communication from Magellan.

[51] In a letter to the Academy of Bordeaux, dated September 14, 1776, Rozier writes: "Permettes que je vous prie, Monsieur, d'engager votre académie à me communiquer ses mémoires interressans ou couronnés. Vous pourres me les faire parvenir sans frais si vous aves la bonté de faire deux envéloppes. Sur l'intérieure cachetée avec du pain à cacheter, il ne faut Ecrire que ces seuls mots *journal de physique* et sur l'exterieure cachetée de la cire d'espagne mettre cette adresse—à MM *de Trudaine intendant général des finances en son hotel à Paris*" (Bibliothèque de Bordeaux, MS 828, XXI, no. 57).

Magellan's established channel of communication. Moreover, we should not underestimate Rozier's own interest in the newly revealed world of British pneumatic chemistry, for chemistry—including the early pneumatic chemistry of Stephen Hales—was an area in which he had some competence as a scientist, as his work on vinification testifies. It need hardly be added that if Trudaine and Magellan had urged him to publish such a series of translations and abridgments on such an important and timely question, he would certainly have found the idea precisely in line with his editorial purpose.

Be that as it may, when Rozier published in August, 1772, his translation of Priestley's *Directions*—both in his journal and as a separate brochure—this proved the first effective step in arousing the curiosity of French chemists about this promising new field of investigation,[52] the more so because Rozier, with a pardonable display of national pride, took the occasion to call attention to a neglected French work on the same subject.

As long ago as 1750 Gabriel François Venel, a pupil of

[52] "Manière d'imprégner l'Eau d'air fixe, & de lui communiquer les propriétés de l'Eau de Pyrmont, & de toutes les Eaux minérales, qui sont connues sous le nom d'Acidules ou Aëriennes, par M. J. Priestley," *Introduction aux observations*, II, 323–331. A footnote reads: "Le Public est averti que c'est au zèle de M. de Trudaine pour les Sciences, à la protection dont il veut bien les honorer, & à l'attention vraiment philosophique qu'il donne à tout ce qui peut intéresser l'humanité, qu'il doit la traduction & la publication de cet Ouvrage." Rozier's translation is quite adequate but omits Priestley's dedicatory epistle to the Earl of Sandwich and the author's preface. Notes by Rozier and one by Magellan are appended; the single plate that appeared in the original is given here redrawn and specially engraved. The catalogue of the Bibliothèque Nationale lists the separate printing (in-8°, so not a mere separate) of this Priestley translation. It is evidently this which Trudaine distributed to members of the Academy on August 14.

G. F. Rouelle and at that time director of the private laboratory of the Duc d'Orléans,[53] had read two memoirs before the Academy of Sciences proving that the waters of Selters near Coblentz owed their piquancy and savor to air combined with or dissolved in the water.[54] By various methods—agitation, heating, and the use of the vacuum pump—he had extracted air from the mineral water, leaving it flat and tasteless; and he had prepared an unpleasantly saline imitation of Seltzer water by mixing soda and muriatic acid in a closed bottle of pure water. These experiments aroused little interest,[55] and indeed by 1772

[53] Venel studied medicine at Montpellier and received the M.D. in 1742. Early in his studies he was attracted to chemistry, probably by the lectures of Sébastien Matte, demonstrator in chemistry at the university. As early as 1739 he had acquired a copy of a pioneering work on phlogistic chemistry, J. B. Senac's anonymous *Nouveau cours de chymie suivant les principes de Newton & de Sthall* (2 vols.; Paris, 1723). Venel's inscribed and dated copy of this book is owned by my friend, Mr. W. A. Cole, of Pacific Palisades, California. A revised edition (2 vols.; Paris, 1737) is more common. Senac's authorship of this book, now generally accepted, is confirmed by a letter of Macquer to Torbern Bergman (dated February 22, 1768). This is to be printed in Johan Nordström's forthcoming *Foreign Correspondence of Torbern Bergman*.

The chief biographical source on Venel is E. H. de Ratte's "Eloge de Monsieur Venel," *Observations sur la physique,* 10 (1777), 3–14. An abridged version of this sketch was printed by Baron Des Genettes in *Eloges des académiciens de Montpellier* (Paris, 1811), pp. 194–203. There are further comments on Venel in the eulogy of Venel's collaborator, Jacques Montet, in the same volume, pp. 247–248.

[54] *Mémoires de mathématiques et de physique présentés à l'Académie royale des sciences par divers sçavans, et lus dans ses assemblées,* II (1755), 53–79 and 80–112. Stephen Hales is quoted by Venel on pp. 64 and 66. This is the collection commonly referred to as the *Mémoires des savants étrangers*. See above p. 19.

[55] Venel's work is mentioned in Diderot's *Encyclopédie* in the

Venel had ceased to do creative research and had faded from the scene. Rozier resurrected him by appending to the Priestley translation an "Extrait de deux Mémoires de M. Venel," adding the comment that they proved that the discovery of air in mineral waters "appartient à la Chymie Françoise," and that the same could be said of the "imitation des eaux aerées." To Priestley, he conceded, must go the credit for showing that an air produced by effervescence can be made to pass into water or other fluid by simple agitation, and to the English, notably MacBride, priority for discovering the medical value of "fixed air." These claims on Venel's behalf greatly annoyed Magellan, the admirer and friend of Priestley.[56]

---

article "Minerales, eaux; chym. & med." (X [1765], 534–541), an abridgment of a Latin treatise by Charles Le Roy, Venel's younger colleague at Montpellier; also in Turgot's article "Expansibilité" (VI [1756], 274–285). Macquer briefly noticed Venel's work in his *Dictionnaire de chymie* of 1766 (I, 391). In the same year Demachy attacked Venel's findings, without mentioning him by name, in the paper discussed above. After he became professor of medicine at Montpellier in 1759, Venel published no chemical research, though he gave public lectures in chemistry in the laboratory of Jacques Montet (another Rouelle pupil and a fellow member of the Academy of Montpellier). Rozier in 1772 lamented "l'espèce d'inaction dans laquelle [Venel] semble être tombé" (*Introduction aux observations*, II, 332). However in 1774, impelled by the critical shortage of firewood in the region of Montpellier, Venel wrote his *Instruction sur l'usage de la houille* (Avignon, 1775), a work advocating and explaining the use of coal. This was his last work, for he died on October 29, 1775. For appraisals of his contributions to chemistry see Gmelin, *op. cit.*, II, *passim;* Hoefer, *Histoire de la chimie* (2nd ed.; Paris, 1866–1869), II, 342–343; and, on a special point, J. R. Partington and Douglas McKie, "Historical Studies on the Phlogiston Theory—I. The Levity of Phlogiston," *Annals of Science*, 2 (1937), 380–381.

[56] Magellan wrote to Lavoisier on February 11, 1774, to acknowl-

It was several months before Rozier was able to bring out the next of his translations and abridgments concerned with pneumatic chemistry. But in August, 1772—at a time when, as we have seen, Lavoisier appears to have been unacquainted with the work of Joseph Black—Rozier was well launched on his project. In the September issue of his *Observations* he published the first significant fragment of Blackiana, a brief summary of some of the experiments on latent heat, entitled "Expériences du Docteur Black, sur la marche de la Chaleur dans certaines circonstances."[57] This summary, the earliest account of Black's work on heat to appear on the Continent and the second to appear anywhere,[58] was described by Rozier as communicated from Edinburgh "par un des Disciples du Docteur Black." Who this "disciple" may have been, we do not know, but his communication was probably transmitted by the path already so familiar to us, i.e., via Magellan and Trudaine. That this was the channel of transmission is rendered more than inherently probable by the fact that, in advance of

---

edge receipt of the *Opuscules:* "La note que vous avez faite sur la decouverte de Mr Vennel [*sic*] m'a donné beaucoup de satisfaction. Car je m'avois presque brouillé avec l'Abbé Rozier de ne pas avoir fait justice dans le particulier, attribuant toute l'invention de l'*air fixe* à M. Venel, qui n'a jamais Connu d'autre air, dans les eaux acidules, que l'air Commun. . . . Le Dr Hales avait trouvé bien La meme chose avant lui, et se trompe de meme" (*Oeuvres de Lavoisier—Correspondance*, II [1957], 430).

[57] *Introduction aux observations*, II, 428–431.

[58] Black never published his own work on heat. The earliest account is to be found in an anonymous publication brought out by the printer and bookseller, John Nourse, in London in 1770 entitled *An Enquiry into the General Effects of Heat; with Observations on the Theories of Mixtures.* See McKie and Heathcote, *Discovery of Specific and Latent Heats*, pp. 50–51.

publication, the substance of this abridgment was reported to the Academy of Sciences by Nicolas Desmarest, a close friend of Trudaine and his professional associate in the work of the Bureau de commerce. We shall discuss this episode in more detail in the next chapter, but from Rozier's prefatory remarks Lavoisier and his fellow chemists could learn, perhaps for the first time, of the importance of Black's chemical discoveries:

L'école d'Edimbourg fera époque dans l'Histoire de la Physique, pour s'être principalement occupée du feu & de l'air fixe. Le Docteur Black est celui qui a le plus multiplié les expériences sur ces deux points importans. Nous nous proposons de les rapprocher & d'en former un ensemble instructif, qui puisse donner à nos Compatriotes, une idée de tout le travail de cet Académicien. Comme les expériences suivantes ne roulent que sur un point isolé, nous avons cru devoir les détacher des autres, que nous présenterons le plutôt qu'il sera possible à nos Lecteurs curieux d'expériences, dont les résultats sont aussi piquans que les procédés en sont ingénieux.[59]

It is obvious that Rozier clearly understood the central importance of Black's work and either had in his possession Black's chemical masterpiece or was in the process of obtaining it to have a translation made. Yet it was not until February, 1773, that he was able to print a "précis raisonné" of the work of Nicolas Jacquin, Black's Viennese disciple, and to preface it with a brief but clear account of the discovery of "fixed air." The translation of Black's *Experiments upon Magnesia Alba* eventually appeared

[59] *Introduction aux observations,* II, 428. The whole summary has been recently reprinted from the duodecimo *Observations* by McKie in *Annals of Science,* 13 (1957), 86–89.

in the March and April issues of Rozier's journal.[60]

Thus in the fall of 1772, apart from the earlier book of MacBride, only Priestley's little pamphlet on artificial soda water was available in translation to represent the work of Black and his disciples. Most, if not all, of the papers Rozier subsequently published probably came into his hands between August and December, 1772. But it is not easy to discover precisely when, and to what extent during these months, Lavoisier was able to consult these writings. That he was in touch with Rozier and aware of his activities is certain,[61] and he was probably kept informed by Trudaine or Rozier himself of the information that Magellan was hastening to make available. In mid-August, for example, Lavoisier appears to have had advance notice of the contents of Desmarest's report on Black's latent heat experiments.[62] And by the time he set down his famous memorandum of February 20, 1773, Lavoisier could write as if he had a considerable familiarity with the literature on "fixed air," including a knowledge of works Rozier had not yet printed. In this important document Lavoisier refers, in the precise order of their original publication, to the experiments of Hales, Black, MacBride, Jacquin, Crantz, Priestley, and De Smeth, the last named being the author of a thesis printed only in October, 1772. To be sure, we cannot be certain that Lavoisier had read and carefully assimilated all these

[60] *Observations sur la physique*, 1 (1773), 123–134, 210–220, and 261–275.

[61] Cf. my "Joseph Priestley's First Papers on Gases," *loc. cit.*, pp. 7–8; but I am no longer convinced that Lavoisier "may have had a hand in these translations."

[62] For this episode see below, pp. 92–94, and my "A Lost Memoir of Lavoisier," *loc. cit.*, pp. 128–129.

works, but that is the impression he conveys; for he speaks of them as the separate links of a great chain, which he hoped, by writing a history of previous developments and by carrying out a long series of experiments, to build into a new and revolutionary theory. The evidence, therefore, suggests that Lavoisier acquired most of his knowledge of the work done abroad on the chemistry of air, not before he carried out his famous experiments in the autumn of 1772, but probably during or after these historic months.[63]

We must, therefore, exclude any direct influence of the writings of Black, Jacquin, and Cavendish (a name notably absent from the February memorandum) upon Lavoisier's first steps in the study of air and combustion. On the other hand, Priestley's first little publication on soda water, which aroused keen interest in the subject of "fixed air" and in the earlier book of MacBride, must have had an appreciable effect on Lavoisier, as we know it did on his contemporaries. At least three of Lavoisier's fellow chemists—J. B. M. Bucquet (1746–1780), Hilaire-Marin Rouelle (1718–1779), and Pierre Bayen (1725–1798)— undertook experiments late in 1772 or early in 1773 which dealt directly with the production and properties of "fixed air," and the work of these men reflects the stimulus of Priestley's pamphlet and the discussions it aroused. Bucquet performed his experiments in the laboratory of the Duc de la Rochefoucauld d'Enville, using an improved version of MacBride's apparatus. These experiments, perhaps suggested to him by Lavoisier, convinced him that the air produced by the action of acids on chalk and mild alkalis was the same whatever acid was used; that it was

[63] This was also Meldrum's opinion. See his *Eighteenth Century Revolution in Science*, p. 12.

identical with the air produced in fermentation; and that, though its density and compressibility seemed to differ little from those of atmospheric air, it was chemically distinct not only from common air, but also from the insoluble, inflammable air produced by the action of acids on metals. These results, which Bucquet obtained before he could learn of the work of Cavendish or had read Priestley's "Observations on Different Kinds of Air," were reported to the Academy of Sciences on April 24, 1773. The experiments may have been begun as early as the fall of 1772.[64]

The younger Rouelle's experiments, published the following month (May, 1773) in Roux's *Journal de médecine,* seem also to have been inspired by Priestley's pamphlet, for they dealt with artificial chalybeate waters that could be produced by the action on various iron ores of water impregnated with "fixed air." [65] It seems also to have been

[64] There is evidence to suggest that Lavoisier and Bucquet had begun some sort of collaboration as early as 1772. If so, it is possible that Lavoisier suggested that his younger friend confirm and extend Priestley's findings, as Trudaine had urged. For Bucquet see Balteau, *op. cit.,* VII (1956), 606–607. His memoir, entitled "Experiences physico-chimiques sur l'air qui se dégage des corps dans le temps de leur décomposition et qu'on connaît sous le nom vulgaire d'*air fixé,*" does not seem to have been published. Yet Lavoisier, who with Desmarest was charged with reporting on it, later gave a short account of it in his *Opuscules* (*Oeuvres de Lavoisier,* I, 548–550). The report by Lavoisier and Desmarest, dated June 12, 1773, was found among Lavoisier's papers and published by the editor of the *Oeuvres* (IV, 155–158). Lavoisier's laboratory *registres* show that in the second week of May, 1773, he began to repeat Bucquet's experiments, using Bucquet's improvement of MacBride's apparatus. See Berthelot, *Révolution chimique,* pp. 239 f.

[65] Lavoisier reproduced Rouelle's paper in his *Opuscules* (*Oeuvres de Lavoisier,* I, 538–547). On April 30, 1773—the day

during the same period, 1772–1773, that Bayen obtained "fixed air" by strongly heating samples of spathic iron ore (siderite).[66]

It is important to emphasize that all of these investigations were undertaken at about the time that Lavoisier was turning his attention to the possible role of air in combustion, yet *before* he undertook to explore directly, as these other men were doing, the properties of Black's "fixed air."

That Lavoisier, too, was in some degree influenced by Priestley's pamphlet is quite likely; it was he, as we have seen, who first described this work to the Academy. A few months later he included Priestley in his list of pneumatic chemists in the February memorandum; and this mention of Priestley, as I have shown elsewhere, could only have been for the *Directions* and not, as has usually been thought, for his classic paper, "Observations on Different Kinds of Air," which was not known in Paris until the spring of 1773. Lavoisier apparently did not follow Trudaine's suggestion that he repeat Priestley's experiments; at least there is no evidence that he did; and unlike some of his fellow chemists, he did not turn at once to a

---

that Lavoisier began his reading of what was to become the historical part of the *Opuscules*—the Comte de Milly (1728–1784) read to the Academy a memoir entitled "L'examen de quelques phénomènes attribués à l'air fixe" (*Procès-verbaux*, 92 [1773], fol. 103).

[66] *Opuscules chimiques de Pierre Bayen*, II, 1–40. Bayen read this paper before the Academy of Sciences on June 25, 1774; the experiments, which he had quoted in a memoir on mercury precipitates published in April, 1774, had been carried out earlier "c'est à dire, à l'époque où la question de l'air fixe commençoit à occuper tous les chimistes."

study of the properties of "fixed air." Perhaps, as I have suggested, he urged Bucquet to undertake this task. But the memorandum of August 8, 1772, and the newly discovered memoir on the elements he drafted at about the same time, which I shall discuss in the next chapter, make it clear that he had begun to speculate about "effervescences" and the role that air might play in chemical processes. Perhaps this curiosity about effervescences was in part aroused, and certainly it must have been quickened, by reading Priestley's pamphlet, which had come into his hands in mid-July. But it is more likely that he had already been led to his fruitful hypothesis somewhat earlier by a consideration of Hales's experiments, in connection with a specific problem I shall discuss below. If this is true, the appearance of Priestley's pamphlet, the discussions and experimentation it evoked, together with the growing realization that other and still more significant work had been done in Britain, would merely have convinced him that he was on the right track and that there was no time to lose.

At all events, the evidence is clear that Lavoisier recorded his first interest in the possible role of air in chemical change and embarked on his study of combustion at precisely the time when—through the activities of Magellan, Trudaine, and Rozier—the attention of French chemists was being drawn to the significance of British pneumatic chemistry, yet before they could have known at first hand the important contributions of Joseph Black and Henry Cavendish, and before they could have heard more than vague reports of the epoch-making results Joseph Priestley was at that time readying for the press.

It could hardly have been Priestley, or any other British chemist, whom Lavoisier was to conjure up as a rival when, to assure himself priority, he set down his brilliant discoveries of the autumn of 1772 in the sealed note of November 1. Yet this is what Lavoisier wanted posterity to believe. Years later, when preparing this famous note for publication, he altered—without regard to the Muse of History—the words of its final paragraph.[67] The original document makes it abundantly clear, in the words Lavoisier hurriedly set down at the time, that it was not the British but the French chemists who seemed to be pressing hard upon him and to whom he feared he might inadvertently disclose, before the proper time, something of his discoveries and his theories. In the version that all Lavoisier scholars have been accustomed to quote, he merely states that the novelty of his results had dictated this accepted procedure for protecting his property.[68] But what he actually wrote in the autumn of 1772 was more clumsily phrased and more explicit:

Cette découverte me paroit une des plus interessantes qui ait ete faite depuis Sthal et Comme il est difficile de ne pas laisser entrevoir a Ses amis dans la Conversation quelque chose qui puisse les mettre Sur la voye de la verité j'ay Cru devoir faire le present depost entre les mains de M. le Secretaire de lacademie en attendant que je rende mes experiences publiques.[69]

[67] The reasons for Lavoisier's action are discussed in my forthcoming paper, "A Curious Lavoisier Episode," *Chymia,* in press.

[68] First printed in Lavoisier's posthumous *Mémoires de chimie* (1805), where it appears in a paper dealing with the history of the weight effect in calcined metals, this altered version was reproduced in the *Oeuvres de Lavoisier* (II, 103). It has since been unquestioningly reproduced by Meldrum, McKie, and other Lavoisier scholars.

[69] The original version, which survives in the archives of the Academy of Sciences, was first printed in 1957 by M. René Fric in *Oeuvres de Lavoisier—Correspondance,* II, 389–390. M. Fric did not note the discrepancies between the original and the commonly printed version.

CHAPTER 3

The Origin of Lavoisier's Experiments—Some Theories Examined and Some New Evidence

LET us turn to our second question and ask ourselves what could have led Lavoisier, in the autumn of 1772, to embark on those experiments that eventually elucidated the mysteries of combustion and produced a revolution in chemistry. No satisfactory answer has been proposed by students of Lavoisier's work, though there have been various conjectures as to the influences that might have been exerted upon him.

One plausible suggestion was advanced by A. N. Meldrum and was naturally based on the assumption, which few have questioned, that Lavoisier's curiosity about combustion was first aroused by his interest in phosphorus and sulphur, substances whose peculiar properties fired his imagination and led him to suspect the role of air in

76

combustion.[1] To find the starting point of his speculations, it seemed only necessary to discover what had drawn his attention to these substances.

Meldrum was the first to point out that in May, 1772, Rozier published in his journal a long paper by the Italian scientist, G. F. Cigna, which Meldrum thought might have suggested Lavoisier's work on phosphorus and sulphur, for Cigna reported that when these substances are burned they absorb a notable amount of air. Lavoisier must have seen this paper, Meldrum argued, because the same issue of Rozier's journal contained a memoir by Lavoisier on experiments he had carried out with Macquer and Cadet to ascertain the cause of the destruction of the diamond by heat. I shall postpone a discussion of Cigna's paper, which dealt with a physiological problem—the asphyxiation of animals in vessels containing a limited amount of air—and which mentioned sulphur and phosphorus only incidentally. There is reason to believe, however, as I intend to show, that Lavoisier had not read this paper. Even if he had, Cigna contributed little beyond what had already been reported by Stephen Hales, a writer to whom Cigna was greatly indebted, except to argue *against* an actual absorption of the air in which phosphorus or sulphur are burned.[2]

---

[1] Meldrum, *Eighteenth Century Revolution*, pp. 3–4. Cf. his "Lavoisier's Three Notes on Combustion," *loc. cit.*, pp. 15–16. Meldrum also suggests that an observation of B. G. Sage on the increase in weight of phosphorus when turned into its acid may also have played a part. For this possibility see below, pp. 170–171.

[2] Meldrum, *Eighteenth Century Revolution*, pp. 3–4, and his "Lavoisier's Three Notes on Combustion," *loc. cit.*, p. 16. Cigna's paper, entitled "Dissertation de M. Cigna, sur les causes de l'extinction de la lumière d'une Bougie, & de la mort des Animaux renfermés

At all events, Cigna's paper would appear less promising as a likely influence on Lavoisier if it were shown that the latter was led, in the first instance, to study the combustion of substances other than phosphorus and sulphur and to wonder about the participation of air. This is the thought behind a different explanation: that Lavoisier first encountered the problem of combustion in the course of an investigation of the mysterious disappearance of the diamond when strongly heated.[3] Some of the men who studied the thermal destruction of the diamond during the course of 1771–1772 became convinced that the diamond actually burned away. Since they compared the appearance of the ignited diamond with that of burning sulphur or phosphorus (one chemist even believed the diamond to be a compound of phosphorus), what is more likely than that Lavoisier should have suspected, for some reason, the role of air and have resolved to study the combustion of these substances in closed vessels? The possible influence of the diamond experiments upon Lavoi-

---

dans un espace plein d'air," was first published in Latin in the *Mélanges de philosophie et de mathématique de la Société Royale de Turin*, II (1760–1761), 168–203. For the French version see *Introduction aux observations*, II, 84–105.

[3] In 1932 Meldrum wrote: "All these things—the work on the diamond, the observations of Sage, of Cigna—doubtless had an influence on Lavoisier by turning his mind towards the subject of combustion" ("Lavoisier's Three Notes on Combustion," *loc. cit.*, p. 16). I accepted the diamond theory in my "Continental Reputation of Stephen Hales," *loc. cit.*, pp. 402–403. See also Douglas McKie, *Antoine Lavoisier* (New York, 1952), pp. 97–101; and Duveen and Klickstein, *Bibliography of the Works of Lavoisier*, p. 22, who have written: "There is no doubt that this work on the diamond and the contemporary comments of Sage and others had a profound influence on the orientation of Lavoisier's work and led to his lengthy and complete studies on combustion."

sier's thinking justifies a substantial digression at this point in our argument.

The Diamond Experiments

That a diamond could be destroyed by intense heat was first brought forcibly to the attention of French scientists by the chemist Jean Darcet (1725–1801) in the spring of 1768. With his patron, the Comte de Lauraguais, a pupil of the elder Rouelle and a pioneer in French efforts to duplicate the porcelain of Meissen, Darcet had been exploring the effects of strong heat on a wide variety of mineral substances, using an improved furnace designed by Lauraguais.[4] In a memoir on part of that research, which he read to the Academy of Sciences in May, 1768, Darcet reported the astonishing discovery that two brilliant diamonds—one placed in a porcelain crucible, perfectly covered and sealed, the other in a crucible supplied with a perforated lid—had both vanished totally after intense heating, as one of his listeners observed, "comme auroit pu faire la goutte d'eau la plus pure." [5]

Darcet's results were received at the Academy with

[4] For Darcet see Michel-J. J. Dizé, *Précis historique sur la vie et les travaux de Jean d'Arcet* (Paris, An X); and Georges Cuvier, *Recueil des éloges historiques* (Paris, 1819), I, 165–185. There is a short sketch by E. Doublet, "Jean Darcet," *Procès-verbaux des séances de la Société des sciences physiques et naturelles de Bordeaux* (1926–27) (1928), pp. 25–27.

[5] *Procès-verbaux*, 87 (1768), fol. 72 verso. See also *Second mémoire sur l'action d'un feu égal, violent, et continué pendant plusieurs jours sur un grand nombre de terres, de pierres . . . lu à l'Académie Royale des Sciences, le 7 et 11 mai 1768 par M. d'Arcet* (Paris, 1771), pp. 89–91; and "Extrait de deux Mémoires . . . par M. Darcet, Docteur-Régent de la Faculté de Médecine de Paris," *Introduction aux observations*, I, 108–123.

79

excitement and incredulity.[6] It hardly seemed possible that such an "incorruptible" body as the diamond—which Macquer had only recently described as "très-réfractaire & même apyre," that is, indestructible by fire [7]—could disappear in such fashion. Yet this remarkable effect had, as a matter of record, been observed before. Darcet's experiments gave new significance to the report that two Florentine experimenters of the Grand Duke of Tuscany, in the year 1694–95, had successfully destroyed a diamond with a burning glass, and that, many years later, the Emperor Francis I (1708–1765), the husband of Maria Theresa, had destroyed diamonds in a furnace.[8] Other less illus-

[6] See the report on Darcet's work by Tillet and Daubenton in *Procès-verbaux*, 87 (1768), fols. 90–96.

[7] Macquer, *Dictionnaire de chymie* (ed. 1766), I, 350–351, art. "Diamant."

[8] The experiments carried out for the Grand Duke of Tuscany, Cosimo III (1642–1723), jointly by Giuseppe Averani (1662–1738), a friend of Redi and Magalotti, and a physician, Cipriano Targioni (1672–1748), in which a diamond was destroyed with a burning lens are described in the *Giornale de letterati d'Italia*, 8 (1711), 221–309. For Cosimo's interest in science see R. Galluzzi, *Histoire de Grand Duché de Toscane, sous le gouvernement des Medicis, traduit de l'Italien* (Paris, 1782–1784), VIII, 42–45, 67–69, 94–100, 356–359. William Coxe (*History of the House of Austria* [London, 1847], III, 436–437) records the scientific interests of Emperor Francis I. For the experiments in which the latter caused 6,000 gulden of diamonds and rubies to be heated for twenty-four hours in a furnace and noted the destruction of the diamonds, see the *Hamburgisches Magazin*, 18 (1757), 164 f. Darcet probably learned of these experiments from a long note in the Baron d'Holbach's translation of a work of J. F. Henckel (*Pyritologie, ou histoire naturelle de la pyrite* [Paris, 1760], II, 413). Lavoisier used this note in his "Premier Memoire sur la destruction du diamant par le feu" (*Oeuvres de Lavoisier*, II, 40–44), but erroneously confused Cosimo and Frances I (who was also, for a time, Grand Duke of Tuscany).

trious persons, it soon came to light, had made the same sort of experiment with identical results.[9] Urged by the Academy to explore the matter further, Darcet reported again on August 19, 1770, some new experiments to dis-

---

It is interesting that Lavoisier's mentor and friend, the geologist Guettard, was told of the Austrian experiments in the course of an audience with Francis I at Vienna, between May 26 and June 4, 1760. He recorded the facts in his journal and observed that these curious experiments should be published, and that one must indeed be an emperor to experiment with such precious stones out of scientific curiosity. See his MS "Voyage fait a La suitte de M. le Marquis de Paulmy—Ambassadeur de france aupres Du Roy de Pologne. Par J. E. Guettard Medecin de M. L'ambassadeur," p. 118. I am grateful to Miss Rhoda Rappaport for bringing this passage to my attention and to Mr. Denis I. Duveen for the generous loan of the Guettard diaries in his possession.

[9] In d'Holbach's words (op. cit., p. 412), Boyle "prétend avoir senti les émanations de plusieurs pierres transparentes, & qu'on peut, en un espace de tems très-court, réduire certains diamants au point d'exhaler des vapeurs très-abondantes & très-acres." Lavoisier, on the other hand, found Boyle's statement vague (Oeuvres de Lavoisier, II, 40, and Introduction aux observations, II, 109). Boyle's text is indeed obscure. See his "An Essay about the Origin and Virtues of Gems" (London, 1672), reprinted in The Works of the Honourable Robert Boyle, III, 516–561, especially pp. 543–544. That eccentric worthy, "Sir" John Hill, had demonstrated that a diamond could be destroyed by fire "very many Years ago, to the Late Excellent Lord Granard and Mr. Charles Stanhope, at my house in Bloomsbury; by placing a small diamond in a wind Furnace." See his Theophrastus's History of Stones, With an English Version, and Notes (2nd ed.; London, 1774), pp. 78–79, note a. A certain Haran reported that about 1746 he had heated diamonds hermetically sealed in a vitrified paste of borax (Introduction aux observations, II, 408–409). Newton, who had observed the anomalous refractive index of the diamond, had in effect predicted its combustibility when he said it "probably is an unctuous Substance coagulated." See Opticks (3rd ed.; London, 1721), p. 249; cf. Thomas Thomson, A System of Chemistry, I (1802), p. 47.

cover the effect of excluding air. His observation that a diamond heated in a crucible with a closely fitting cover and one enclosed in a ball of porcelain paste both disappeared when strongly heated made it seem evident, in the words of one report, that "tous les diamans sont volatils par eux-mêmes à un degré de feu assez médiocre, & sans le concours de l'air." [10]

Darcet's destruction of the diamond was widely discussed in scientific circles, reported in the popular press, and repeated by other scientists. In July, 1771, in the presence of "dix-sept personnes très-instruites"—among whom were Darcet and the chemists Bucquet and Rouelle the younger—P. J. Macquer heated in a muffle furnace a diamond enclosed in an open capsule of refractory clay and showed that it vanished after forty minutes of heating.[11]

The phenomenon was now the talk of Paris. A public demonstration was carried out by Darcet and the younger Rouelle in the amphitheater of the Jardin du Roi on August 16, 1771, before a distinguished audience of foreign dignitaries, members of the nobility, men of letters, and savants of the Academy of Sciences, including Macquer and Lavoisier. The pharmacist Mitouard, later to make an interesting contribution to the problem, was also present, as well as a number of Paris jewelers and diamond merchants. The experiments were dramatic and successful; the significance of this spectacular confirmation of Darcet's discovery was widely debated.[12]

[10] *Introduction aux observations*, I, 120.

[11] *Ibid.*, p. 123. Cf. *Journal encyclopédique*, 1771, no. 7, part 2, p. 287.

[12] The *procès-verbal* of these experiments was published by Rozier in January, 1772 (*Introduction aux observations*, I, 484–488).

Several months later a less lavish public demonstration was made by Darcet's friend, Dr. Augustin Roux, the physician of Mlle de Lespinasse, at the Ecole de médecine on April 23, 1772. Before a large audience in the lecture hall of the school and in the presence (it was meticulously noted) of M. de Sartine, the Lieutenant General of Police, Roux carried out the destruction of two diamonds. In the course of this demonstration Roux called attention to an effect which others had already noted but not particularly stressed: namely, that at one point the diamond could be shown to be actually burning. Macquer had observed the diamond glowing brightly "d'une lumière comme phosphorique,"[13] and at the Jardin du Roi it had been seen to take on at one moment a "couleur très resplendissante." But Roux's observation was more striking, for on opening the door of the furnace as the experiment progressed he clearly saw a flame and "annonça hautement à l'assemblée que le diamant brûloit effectivement, & il le fit remarquer à deux on trois personnes qui se trouvoient alors à côté du fourneau."[14]

A brief account had already appeared in the *Journal encyclopédique,* 1771, no. 7, part 2, pp. 286–292. See also Bachaumont, *Mémoires secrets,* 5, 359, under the date of August 28, 1771.

[13] *Introduction aux observations,* I, 123. B. G. Sage likewise reported that a diamond he had exposed to the fire "a répandu des vapeurs âcres, accompagnées d'une lumière distincte, qui formoit une auréole autour de lui; pendant ce temps il a changé de forme, peu après il a disparu." He went so far as to assert that the diamond was a compound of phosphoric acid and a fixed alkali. See his *Elémens de minéralogie docimastique,* p. 132.

[14] "Expériences nouvelles, sur la destruction du Diamant dans les vaisseaux fermés, par Messieurs d'Arcet & Rouelle," *Observations sur la physique,* 1 (1773), 25. Cf. the brief account in the *Journal encyclopédique,* 1771, no. 7, part 2, p. 287.

Now that the phenomenon of the diamond's disappearance was settled beyond a doubt, various rival theories were advanced to account for it. Darcet himself believed that the diamond was inherently volatile, passing off as a kind of vapor, for he thought his experiments had shown that air was not necessary to produce the effect. Others were convinced that upon contact with cold air the heated diamond fractured and decrepitated into an invisible powder. Still others—among them Macquer, Mitouard, and Roux—suspected that it was destroyed by a kind of combustion, "semblable à celle qu'on remarque dans le phosphore & dans quelques autres substances." [15]

This difference of opinion, it was realized, had to be resolved by new experiments. In accord with the Academy's policy that such important questions should be investigated in common, Macquer, Cadet, and Lavoisier early in 1772 combined their efforts, using the facilities of Cadet's laboratory. Since Darcet's results with his balls of porcelain made the decrepitation and combustion theories seem unlikely, they set out to test the remaining hypothesis. If, they argued, the diamond is truly volatile and produces vapors or fumes, these should be detectable by distillation; and if it is not volatile but combustible or otherwise unstable in the presence of air—though Darcet's inaccurate experiments had suggested that air was unnecessary—then it should resist destruction when intensely heated in closed vessels. [16]

A glimpse of these experimenters at work has been afforded us by a noble "curieux," the Duc de Croÿ, who wrote in his journal:

[15] *Introduction aux observations,* II, 108–109.
[16] *Ibid.,* p. 109.

J'allai chez M. Cadet, apothicaire, où on faisait encore l'expérience du diamant. J'y trouvai les fourneaux allumés et tout le monde bien occupé. C'est M. Lavoisier, fermier général et membre de l'Académie, et un autre qui essayaient de distiller le diamant, puisqu'on pouvait le volatiliser, comme on l'avait prouvé par beaucoup d'expériences, et une fameuse, il y avait six mois, chez M. Rouelle.

J'y retournai à sept heures du soir, et il résulta que les diamants ne furent point altérés, parce qu'ils étaient enfermés dans des cornues et qu'ils ne se brulent et dissipent bien qu'à l'air libre. Cela mit en train de mettre bien des diamants au feu! [17]

The old soldier's account, though vivid, is a little vague and confused, and it is not easy to know precisely which experiments he is talking about; but Lavoisier has given his own account of the attempt to distill the diamond—an approach which seems to have interested him particularly—with his typical clarity. He and his associates took a number of diamond fragments and small diamonds and placed them in a small retort of stoneware (*grès*). When the retort was strongly heated for three hours in Cadet's

[17] *Journal inédit du Duc de Croij* (*1718–1784*), ed. E. H de Grouchy and P. Cottin (Paris, 1906–1907), III, 19. A distinguished military man, veteran of Ramillies, Raucoux, and Lawfeld, the Duc de Croÿ had commanded the cavalry at the siege of Bergen-op-zoom. In 1763 he directed the restoration of the port of Dunkirk. After his retirement he devoted himself to the study of chemistry and mineralogy. In a letter of Dupain-Triel to Lavoisier (April 25, 1771) he is mentioned as anxious to learn more about Lavoisier's geological work (*Oeuvres de Lavoisier—Correspondance*, II, 320–321). Letters from the Duc de Croÿ survive in the Macquer correspondence. In 1782 he published his *Mémoire sur le passage du Nord;* the year following he received the baton of a Marshal of France; he died at Paris on March 30, 1784.

assay furnace, the diamonds were found to have lost one-seventh of their weight, but nothing was collected in the receiver except a little water from the luting material.[18]

Another, and more significant, experiment was carried out to see if the diamond really resisted destruction when air was excluded. A skilled jeweler, named Maillard, convinced that the diamond could not be destroyed except in contact with air, contributed three diamonds to the experimenters on condition that he be allowed to arrange for the exclusion of air. He inserted the diamonds in a clay pipestem, filled it with ground charcoal, and closed the ends with lute; the pipestem was then placed in a crucible surrounded by powdered chalk and this in turn was put inside two larger crucibles set mouth to mouth and firmly sealed together. When this Chinese-box device was subjected to the strongest attainable heat, the crucible was badly deformed; although the pipestem resisted the heat, it was found to have changed into a porcelain which had fused with the surrounding chalk. Yet when the pipestem was broken open, the charcoal was as black as ever, and the diamonds were found unaltered. As we shall see, even more suggestive experiments of this sort were performed soon after by a certain Mitouard, a Paris pharmacist and public lecturer in chemistry.[19]

Lavoisier, evidently the most energetic though the

[18] "Résultat de quelques expériences faites sur le diamant, par MM. Macquer, Cadet & Lavoisier, lu à la Séance Publique de l'Académie Royale des Sciences, le 29 Avril 1772." *Introduction aux observations*, II, 109–110. See also *Journal encyclopédique*, 1772, no. 4, part 1, pp. 268–274.

[19] "Résultat des Expériences faites le 30 Avril 1772 sur le Diamant & sur plusieurs Pierres précieuses, lu à l'Académie Royale des Sciences, le 2 Mai 1772, par M. Mitouard, Démonstrateur en Chymie, & maître en Pharmacie à Paris," *Introduction aux observations*, II, 112–116. On Mitouard see below, pp. 173–191.

86

youngest and least experienced of the three experimenters, was chosen to present an account of this work to a *séance publique* of the Academy on Wednesday, April 29, 1772. These results—though the distillation experiment had been inconclusive—indicated strongly that the diamond is not attackable by heat except in the presence of air. When air is excluded, especially if the diamond is protected by powdered charcoal, the diamond is "absolument fixe." And Lavoisier's report concluded:

Ce phénomène ne doit point s'attribuer à une véritable volatilization, comme on le pensoit; mais plutôt à une espèce de combustion, comme celle du charbon, & de quelques autres substances qui résistent, comme lui, à la violence du feu dans les vaisseaux fermés, ou bien que cet effet est dû à une réduction des parties du diamant en une poudre très-fine, occasionnée par le contact de l'air. Nous nous proposons de nous assurer, par de nouvelles expériences, à laquelle de ces deux opinions on doit s'arreter.[20]

This passage has been taken as evidence that Lavoisier strongly suspected that the diamond burned and may thereby have been led on to explore the combustion of "similar" substances, like phosphorus and sulphur. Unfortunately, Lavoisier's official report on behalf of his collaborators conceals a striking lack of unanimity. Macquer, like the jeweler Maillard and the pharmacist Mitouard, was convinced that the diamond burned. Cadet, on the other hand, favored the theory that the diamond

---

[20] *Introduction aux observations*, II, 111. Besides the experiments of Darcet, the strongest argument for believing in a true volatilization was the statement of Boyle, frequently cited by French workers on the diamond, that he had noted abundant acrid vapors when it was strongly heated. See above, this chap., notes 9 and 13.

decrepitated. Lavoisier, it will be seen, differed from both his colleagues and, I feel sure, privately dissented from what he wrote in the joint memoir concerning the impossibility of distilling the diamond.

We can learn something of Lavoisier's own personal expectations by referring once again to the August memorandum of 1772, with its suggestions for experiments with the burning glass. Here, in a section entitled "Expériences à tenter sur le diamant," he completely ignores the possibility of the diamond's being consumed by combustion. Like his coworkers of the previous spring he considers the decrepitation theory worthy of consideration; but unlike Macquer and Cadet—whose majority opinion he had been obliged to set forth in his memoir—he clearly does not believe the volatility of the diamond to have been disproved, for the burden of this section of the August memorandum is to propose an experiment to decide between the two possibilities he evidently favored and to learn whether (1) the diamond evaporates and is "véritablement volatile," or whether (2) it decrepitates in contact with cold air. Lavoisier says nothing about demonstrating the possibility of a combustion, and the experiment has no such objective. He suggests placing a sizable diamond at the bottom of a deep crucible of rock crystal and exposing the uncovered diamond to the focus of a powerful burning glass. Should the diamond decrepitate, it would be found to break into thin fragments, some of which would remain in the crucible. If it should prove to be volatile, absolutely nothing would be left behind.[21] In-

[21] *Oeuvres de Lavoisier*, III, 264. A similar proposal had been made by Mitouard in his paper of May 2, 1772, and Lavoisier may be echoing it, though Mitouard's purpose was probably to decide

terestingly enough, Lavoisier and his coworkers actually carried out an experiment of this sort ten days later (on August 18, 1772) which seemed to suggest that the diamond decrepitated.[22] It is pretty clear that in the summer of 1772 Lavoisier—unlike some of his confrères—did not believe the diamond to be combustible. Thus the theory about the origin of Lavoisier's work which I once advanced rather strongly appears to have little to support it.

In the August memorandum, finally, there is no mention of experiments with phosphorus or sulphur, let alone any suggestion of comparing these substances with the diamond. I can, in sum, see no bridge between Lavoisier's

---

between combustion and decrepitation. See *Introduction aux observations*, II, 115–116. The decrepitation theory had been advanced long before by the Florentine experimenters, and later by "Sir" John Hill, who attributed a laminar structure to the diamond and wrote that the heated diamond "shivered and cracked in many places, and afterwards became smaller and smaller till it entirely vanished" (*Theophrastus's History of Stones*, pp. 78–79). Hill's observation was known to Lavoisier; the work had appeared in French translation in 1754.

[22] "Détail des expériences exécutées au moyen du grand verre ardent," *Oeuvres de Lavoisier*, III, 292. This experiment of August 18, 1772 (30ᵉ expérience) was the only one on the diamond carried out with the burning glass in that year. A year later (August, 1773) a number of diamond experiments were performed, for even then Lavoisier and his associates were not convinced at first that the diamond actually burned, but they were led to this conclusion as a result of experiments showing the blackening of the heated diamonds. See especially Exper. 220 (August 14, 1773), *ibid.*, pp. 341–342. It was in the autumn of 1773 that experiments were performed in collaboration with Macquer, proving that "fixed air" is produced when a diamond burns. This experiment is recorded in Lavoisier's so-called "missing" *registre* and in Lavoisier's second memoir on the destruction of the diamond (*Oeuvres de Lavoisier*, II, 74–77). The memoir was actually written in June, 1774. See Lavoisier papers, archives of the Academy of Sciences, Paris, dossier 72-D and 72-K.

investigations of the diamond and his experiments on combustion. Instead I shall try, in the course of this study, to show that a quite different sort of problem led him to speculate about the role of air in combustion, to wonder about the adequacy of the phlogistic explanation, and to carry out his famous experiments of the autumn of 1772.

Effervescence and a Theory of the Elements

Here again the August memorandum can help us understand Lavoisier's train of thought during the summer of 1772. A careful reading of its concluding section ("Sur l'air fixe, ou plutôt sur l'air contenu dans les corps") brings to light the phenomenon that encouraged Lavoisier to assert so confidently that air enters into the composition of most mineral substances, even of metals, and in great abundance. This was the commonly observed, but mysterious, phenomenon of chemical effervescence. An effervescence, Lavoisier went on to explain, is the result of a sudden release of air; air is given off in chemical reactions whenever the resulting compound contains less of it than is supplied by the reacting substances.

Such effervescences were of course familiar occurrences in the laboratory and were commonly observed by all chemists when they treated chalk, limestone, or the mild alkalis (carbonates) with acid, or exposed metals (especially iron) to the action of dilute acid. As a striking example, the inflammable fumes produced by treating iron with dilute acid had been vividly described by Robert Boyle and by chemical authors of the eighteenth century. But the real nature of these effervescences was obscured by a common habit of speaking, in vague terms, of vapors, spirits, or fumes. Nor were they closely examined by Continental chemists, even by those who had pneumatic apparatus at their disposal or who—influenced by Stephen Hales—admitted that effervescences might be due to the release of air.

In his *Vegetable Staticks* Hales described many of these familiar reactions; he had collected and measured the "true air" produced, but did not explicitly discuss chemical effervescences in his book, nor even commonly use the term. But in an appendix which he prepared for a second edition of this work (and which was added instead to his *Haemastaticks* of 1733), he cited at length some experiments of Musschenbroek on effervescent mixtures and explained them in terms of his theory of fixable air. This appendix was translated by Buffon and included in his French version of the *Vegetable Staticks* (1735); Hales's explanation was therefore frequently referred to in France. Venel, for example, adopted it in his article "Effervescence" in Diderot's *Encyclopédie,* giving Hales as his authority.[23] And Macquer wrote in the first edition of his *Dictionnaire de chymie* that "les effervescences sont accompagnées de bulles, de petits jets, de vapeurs, & d'une sorte de bruit ou de frémissement; tous ces phénomènes sont dûs à de l'air qui se dégage, ou qui se développe dans presque toutes les dissolutions."[24] Yet apparently Macquer made little application of this theory, for when he discusses the solution of iron in dilute vitriolic acid, he does not mention that an inflammable air is given off but merely says that the vapors from the effervescence are heavily charged with phlogiston, as is proved by their great inflammability. Lavoisier, as will

---

[23] *Encyclopédie,* V (1755), 404–405.
[24] *Dictionnaire de chymie* (ed. 1766), I, 397–398.

appear, was the first French chemist to apply the idea in a general way to an understanding of specific reactions. His speculations are embodied in a newly discovered and most important document which has an interesting relationship to his August memorandum. To appreciate its importance, a little background must be supplied.

In a recent paper I tried to clarify the nature of the August memorandum and to demonstrate that it had long been confused with a lost memoir on heat, a "Mémoire sur le feu élémentaire," in which it appeared that Lavoisier might have set down some interesting speculations on heat.[25] This memoir, or something like it, had evidently been initialed by the Secretary of the Academy on August 19, ten days before Nicolas Desmarest read to the Academy a *précis* of some of Joseph Black's unpublished discoveries on latent heat. That Desmarest read the same document Rozier published soon after in the September issue of his journal, under the title "Expériences du Docteur Black, sur la marche de la Chaleur dans certaines circonstances," [26] is evident from the Academy's minutes for the meeting of August 29, where we read: "M. —— a lu des experiences sur la marche de la Chaleur dans certaines circonstances faites à Edimbourg par M. de Dr Watch [*sic*]." [27]

It was Desmarest who read the *précis*, as we learn from Lavoisier, who hastened to publish a brief account of some earlier experiments of his own. In the course of

[25] "A Lost Memoir of Lavoisier," *loc. cit.*, pp. 125–129. This article appeared in the issue of June, 1959.

[26] See above, pp. 68–69.

[27] *Procès-verbaux*, 91 (1772), fol. 304 recto. My attention was called to this passage by my student, Mr. Roger Hahn.

these he had observed certain thermal effects, similar to those reported by Black, in the melting of ice and in ice-water mixtures. His results were summarized in the October issue of Rozier's journal as a commentary on Black's experiments.

It seemed very likely that Lavoisier had heard something at the earlier meeting of August 19—perhaps a preliminary announcement of Black's results—which led him to leave the meeting abruptly to fetch his unpublished "Mémoire sur le feu élémentaire" for the Secretary to initial. Though there is no reference to Black's work or to Desmarest, who was present, in the Secretary's minutes for that meeting, it is not difficult to reconstruct what probably happened. Grandjean de Fouchy, the Secretary, records that he read to the Academy two papers (*deux dépots*) which had been entrusted to the Academy, in 1755 and 1757, by the celebrated Abbé Nollet. The first does not concern us, but the second dealt with the chilling of vessels by the evaporation of liquids. This evidently gave rise to some discussion, though what was said is not recorded in the minutes. But in the course of the discussion I think Desmarest may have remarked on the interesting, and somewhat related, discoveries of Joseph Black, which Rozier was readying for publication. Perhaps Desmarest was invited to report on this work of Black to a later meeting of the Academy. At all events, something of the kind must have led Lavoisier to leave the meeting and bring back his memoir, for Fouchy noted: "M. Lavoisier a dit qu'il avait un *mémoire sur le feu élémentaire*. Il est sorti pour l'aller chercher. Il l'a rapporté et je l'ai paraphé à l'instant." [28] Lavoisier did not disclose the contents or the

[28] *Ibid.*, fol. 292 recto and verso.

93

tenor of this document, but he clearly refers to it in the short paper published by Rozier in October. Here, in commenting on the results he claimed to have observed "dans le courant de Septembre de l'année dernière," i.e., in 1771, Lavoisier wrote:

Je crois être en état de rendre une raison satisfaisante de ce phénomène [the latent heat of fusion]: mais comme l'explication que j'en donnerois tient à un *système sur les élémens, & qui est déja paraphé par M. de Fouchy,* je remets à en entretenir l'Académie dans un autre tems.[29]

What could Lavoisier mean by his "système sur les élémens," which he said that Fouchy had initialed? Could it have been the same document the Secretary referred to as Lavoisier's "Mémoire sur le feu élémentaire"? The answer seemed to be probably yes, there being no evidence that Fouchy in these months had initialed any other memoir for Lavoisier. Perhaps the memoir on heat was part of a larger and more ambitious treatment of the *élémens.* If so, it was probable that by this word Lavoisier meant the classic Four Elements or peripatetic principles: Fire, Air, Water, and Earth; for, as I have indicated above, the discoveries of Stephen Hales had made it seem likely that air ought to be restored as an elementary principle, and this in turn had led to a cautious revival of the old theory of the Four Elements. This theory, we have seen, was held, or at least considered as a likely possibility, by the elder Rouelle and by Macquer. Baumé, Macquer's disciple, and perhaps others, shared the same opinion.[30]

[29] *Introduction aux observations,* II, 510–511. The emphasis is the present writer's.
[30] See above, pp. 33–34.

That Lavoisier had indeed written something about air as an element is evident from his August memorandum.[31] After the important passages about the air found in mineral substances and produced by chemical effervescence, Lavoisier wrote (according to the version printed from the corrected manuscript): "Ces vues suivies et approffondies pourroient conduire à une théorie intéressante qu'on a même déjà ébauchée. . . ." But inspection of the original document shows that Lavoisier had substituted this sentence for an even stronger statement: "On ne Suivra pas ces Vues plus loin, elles font le Sujet d'un travail deja fort avancé, meme en partie redigé." This offered reliable proof that Lavoisier had somewhere set down, probably in what he called his "Système sur les élémens," a more elaborate account of his views on air briefly alluded to in the August memorandum.

In my paper I did not pursue the subject of Lavoisier's early memoir on air but only attempted to reconstruct what his views on elementary fire might have been. Because of the character of Lavoisier's experiments on melting ice and the similarities he discerned between his own work and Black's discoveries on latent heat, it seemed probable that this lost memoir contained an early version of his later caloric theory. If so, he would have described heat as a fire fluid capable of existing in two forms or states: one free (*feu libre*), capable of influencing the thermometer, the other latent or combined (*feu combiné*). This is the theory he was later to elaborate in his memoir of 1777. I did not at first perceive that he might have imagined other elements—air and water for example—as likewise existing in two forms, fixed and free, or that his

[31] See pp. 102–104 and Appendix III.

speculations on free and combined fire might have led him to an interest in Hales's and Priestley's work on fixed air. Yet this seems to have been the case, as the recent surprising discovery of his "Système sur les élémens" makes abundantly clear.

In September, 1959, M. Maurice Daumas reported the discovery by M. René Fric, editor of Lavoisier's *Correspondance*, of three hitherto unknown documents in the hand of Lavoisier.[32] Two of these date from the year 1773 and, though interesting, are too late to concern us here. The other, dated August, 1772, is of great importance; it is fourteen pages long and consists of the much corrected drafts of two incomplete memoirs, followed by two brief notes on two pages of smaller format. The first memoir, entitled "Refflexions sur lair et sur sa combinaison dans les mineraux," is three and a half pages long; the second, "Refflexions sur la combinaison de la matierre du feu dans les corps," devotes three pages to his theory of heat and four to the role of water in chemical combination and to its change of state. In the first of the concluding notes Lavoisier remarks on certain effervescent reactions that produce cold rather than heat. The second consists only of two introductory paragraphs for a projected memoir on the relation of air to the matter of fire. This strange assemblage is consecutively paginated, with each page bearing the stylish initials of the Secretary of the Academy of Sciences. It closes with the significant notation by Lavoisier: "voyes mes idées Sur les elemens." Immediately following on the last page is the attestation by Fouchy: "Le 19 Aoust 1772 M. Lavoisier m'a presenté

[32] At the Colloque international sur l'histoire de la chimie au XVIIIe siècle, held at Paris, September 11–13, 1959.

(La) present [modèle] mémoire pour estre paraphé ce que Jay fait et le luy ay rendu." Beyond a doubt, this is the "Système sur les élémens" to which Lavoisier referred in his October memoir in Rozier's journal and the same document that Fouchy called Lavoisier's "Mémoire sur le feu élémentaire." [33]

Incomplete and tentative though this document is, we can see quite clearly the direction of Lavoisier's thought and the theory he has plainly adopted. He argues that all substances contain their proper portion of air, fire, and water, and that these elementary principles have the property of existing in two forms, fixed or free. When fixed, each is combined with the other elements in an amount characteristic of each substance; in this state these elements do not possess the properties associated with them in the free state. Fire, for example, when combined, does not affect the thermometer, but in the free state it exists as a fluid which penetrates the pores of bodies "et qui Se met a peu pres en equilibre dans chacun deux et dont la plus ou moins grande intensité produit les differens degres de chaleur." The resemblance to Black's theory is striking; moreover, Lavoisier's words anticipate in remarkable fashion his own later doctrine of caloric. By his theory the drop in temperature observed when a fluid evaporates is easily explained: the vapor, which is a combination of the particles of the fluid with the matter of fire, has drawn this fire from the remaining fluid and from the vessel, lowering the temperature. Likewise, in

[33] For this document see René Fric, "Contribution à l'étude de l'évolution des idées de Lavoisier sur la nature de l'air et sur la calcination des métaux," *Archives internationales d'histoire des sciences*, 12, no. 47 (1959; published early in 1960), 137–168.

what we would today call exothermic chemical reactions, some of the matter of fire is set free because the end products contain less fire than the starting materials. Conversely, a cooling effect is observed in cases where the final products require more matter of fire than the reactants can supply and so take it up from the surroundings.

For the purpose of this study, Lavoisier's reflections on air are of still greater interest, for much that he says is concisely echoed in the August memorandum. Many experiments, he begins, seem to prove that air "entre pour beaucoup dans la Composition des mineraux." Yet these experiments—he is probably referring chiefly to those of Hales—have been generally ignored and have left no mark on chemical theory. The old definitions of minerals have remained unchanged and chemists "ny ont point fait entrer lair." He intends, he says, to summarize this evidence, which he has carefully verified by his own experiments.

The reactions that most clearly reveal the participation of air are those in which effervescence occurs, for he remarks, as in the August memorandum, that an effervescence "nest autre chose qu'un degagement Subit dair." Air is presumably contained in all bodies. When two substances react together there may be evolution of air (when the product requires less of it than is supplied by the reactants) or absorption of air (if the product requires more) or neither absorption nor release of air (if the product contains just the amount the reacting substances are able to supply). This, he points out, closely resembles the behavior of the matter of fire.

Lavoisier's concrete examples are disappointingly few and brief; evidently, what we have is only the beginning of a memoir that he never completed. The action of mineral acids on chalk and on the weak alkalis (carbonates) and the action of acids on metals are the familiar examples he gives of chemical reactions yielding a notable amount of air. But does the air come from the acid, rather than from the base? Lavoisier thinks not, because it is possible to alter the base (the earth or the metal) so that it will not yield air when treated with acid. Whereas if the property of producing effervescence resided in the acid, air should be produced despite the use of a different base. He then cites certain examples of "combinations" that *absorb* air, notably a solution of quicklime in water.

These examples are quickly disposed of, and Lavoisier turns again to the analogy between the absorption and release of air and the similar effects observed with the matter of fire. In most reactions involving effervescence there is also a transfer of the fire matter. Some reactions, as when acids act on chalk, produce an effervescence accompanied by heat; in others a pronounced cooling accompanies the release of air. This, we have seen, Lavoisier explained by the amount of fire matter that enters into the composition of the final product. But it is clear that another factor is involved. In his short concluding note, "Refflexions sur lair," he tries to explain how a highly expansible fluid like air can also exist in fixed form, occupying in a solid substance a space six hundred times less than it takes up in the atmosphere. What he calls his "theorie Singuliere" is that the air we breathe is not a simple substance but a combination or compound of a particular fluid with the matter of fire. The air released in effervescences, like the vapors of which he has already spoken, are combinations of the fluid substance with particles of the matter of fire. The reader need hardly be reminded that this theory was later adapted by Lavoisier when he came to characterize the newly described gases making up common air. It is surprising to find this theory so clearly formulated at such an early stage of Lavoisier's career.

Inspection of this remarkable document raises a number of important questions. When, first of all, was it written, and when were the experiments he refers to actually performed? What led him to his theory concerning air? What bearing does all this have, besides confirming Lavoisier's interest in the chemistry of air in the summer of 1772, on the combustion experiments he was to perform the following autumn?

Each page of our document bears the date "Aoust 1772," but this may have been added when it was initialed by Fouchy. Because certain of the ideas contained in it are reflected in the August memorandum, where he also speaks of his speculations on air as "en partie redigé," it must have been written before August 8, 1772. But how much earlier? Unless new evidence turns up, we are limited to conjecture. It is possible that Lavoisier had begun to meditate upon the problem of air not long after the experiments on melting ice had been performed in September, 1771, for we have seen how closely connected in his mind were his ideas about fire and about air. But I doubt if his theory was formulated quite so early, at least as concerns air. It was probably the first news of Priestley's discoveries, vague though they were, but more especially the appearance in France of Priestley's *Directions,* that aroused his interest in air and effervescences, led him to turn to Hales's *Vegetable Staticks* for more information, and induced him to perform those experiments to which he refers at the beginning of his "Système sur les élémens." If this is correct, the experiments were probably performed in the latter part of July, because it was in this month that Trudaine brought Priestley's work to Lavoisier's attention and urged him to repeat some of Priestley's experiments in the *Directions;* and it was Lavoisier who, soon after, read Magellan's letter to a meeting of the Academy. We may conjecture, then, that the "Système sur les élémens" was written late in July or in the first week of August, for the experiments referred to are too few, if not too trivial, to suggest that he had been long at work on his effervescent reactions. I incline to believe, moreover, that Lavoisier merely extended to "fixed air" the theory he had earlier developed (on the basis of the experiments of September, 1771) that the matter of fire existed in two forms; he had perhaps already compared this behavior of fire with that of water, which exists both free and as water of crystallization. It was probably the discussions of "fixed air" in July, 1772, that led him to perceive the great analogy of which he speaks and to extend his theory to encompass the behavior of air.

Lavoisier's "Système sur les élémens" makes it crystal clear that the phenomenon of effervescence, observed in a number of common inorganic reactions, had convinced him, by the early summer of 1772, that air must play an important role in chemical processes. Yet there is no suggestion in this interesting document that air might be chemically involved in combustions or calcinations; indeed, such processes are not so much as mentioned. But by the time he set down the memorandum of August 8, 1772, this possibility had clearly occurred to him. If this is true, it would seem to follow that calcination and reduction of metals, not combustion in the usual sense (in particular, not the combustion of phosphorus) supplied the starting point for his immensely fruitful investigations of the following autumn. This possibility has been overlooked or discounted; without exception, Lavoisier scholars seem to have fallen into the snare unwittingly set for them by the sealed note of November 1, where Lavoisier stated that his experiments on the reduction of minium had been prompted by his success with phosphorus and sulphur. Some rather persuasive evidence must be marshaled if we are to set aside so audaciously this testimony from Lavoisier's own pen. Fortunately for our hypothesis, the great chemist is the best witness to the inaccuracy of his own statement.

Once again, we must turn to the August memorandum. In the brief introduction to this document Lavoisier introduces the subject of calcination; he speaks, without enthusiasm, of the theory of Stahl "sur le phlogistique et sur la réduction des métaux" and then suggests that the use of the burning glass should make it possible to determine whether metals can be calcined in closed vessels, a point of obvious significance to him, as we shall see. The subject of calcinations and reductions is reverted to again in the concluding section, from which I have already quoted. But because Lavoisier's approach to the problem is rather vague and oblique, I think it worth while to reproduce this section in its entirety from the original manuscript, rather than from the printed version.

Sur l'air fixe, ou plutot
Sur l'air Contenu dans les Corps

Il paroit Constant que (la pluspart) l'air entre dans la Composition de la plus part des Mineraux, *des Metaux meme Et en tres grande abondance.* aucun chimiste Cependant n'a fait encore entrer l'air dans la definition ni des Metaux ni d'aucun corps mineral. une effervescence n'est autre chose qu'un degagement Subit de l'air qui etoit en quelque façon dissout dans chacun des Corps que l'on Combine.

Ce degagement a lieu toutes les fois qu'il entre moins d'air dans la Combinaison du nouveau Composé qu'il n'entroit dans chacun des deux corps qui entrent dans la Combinaison. (on ne Suivra pas Ces Vues plus loin, elles sont le Sujet d'un travail deja fort avancé meme en partie Redigé) *Ces vues Suivies et approffondies pourroient Conduire a une theorie interessante qu'on a meme deja ebauchée,* mais ce qui doit ici fixer l'attention, c'est que la plus part des Metaux ne font plus d'effervescence lors qu'ils ont été tenus longtemps au feu du Miroir ardent. Sans doute que le degré de Chaleur qu'ils y eprouvent leur enleve l'air qui entroit dans leur Combinaison. ce qui est tres particulier, c'est que les metaux dans cet etat ne Sont plus malleables Et qu'ils Sont presqu'indissolubles dans les acides. cette observation qui a encore besoin de Confirmation, peut fournir une ample matierre a observations Et a Reflexions.

il Seroit bien a desirer qu'on put appliquer au Verre ardent l'appareil de M. halles [*sic*] pour mesurer la quantité d'air *produitte ou absorbée dans chaque operation,* mais on craint que les difficultés que presentent ce genre d'experiences ne Soit insurmontable au Verre ardent.[34]

[34] Lavoisier papers, archives of the Academy of Sciences, Paris. The words deleted by Lavoisier are placed in parentheses; his emendations and additions are given in italics. I wish to thank the officials of the Academy and Mme Gauja for providing me with a photograph of this document.

There are several things in this text worthy of attention besides the reference to the phenomenon of effervescence in connection with the behavior of metals. It is apparent that Lavoisier's earlier study of effervescences had made it seem likely that metals contain air, which can be released by treatment with acids. But what happens when a metal is transformed into its calx by exposure to sunlight in the focus of a burning glass? According to Stahl, it must simply lose phlogiston. Lavoisier suggests, however, that the heat may drive off the combined air, for this might explain the loss of malleability and of solubility in acids. Clearly, he is uncertain as to what takes place: he is only clear that air must be involved in some way in this transformation of a metal into its calx. Was it possible, as the last paragraph seems to imply, that air might be *absorbed*, rather than produced, during this calcination? To answer this question he proposes to subject metals and their calxes in a closed vessel to the heat of a burning glass, using some form of Hales's pedestal apparatus.

Is there stronger evidence than the August memorandum that Lavoisier had come to suspect, in the face of the observation that treating metals with acids produces air, that metals might *absorb* air in being transformed into their calxes? The answer is supplied by Lavoisier himself in a passage he set down later and which students of his work seem to have overlooked. It makes apparent, I think, how Lavoisier was led from his study of effervescences in solution to speculations about the role of air in combustion; and it suggests that Lavoisier took more seriously than the August memorandum implies the possibility that air, rather than being released from a metal on calcination, actually combines with it. In a memoir entitled "Réflexions sur le phlogistique," read in 1783 and published three years later, Lavoisier wrote:

Une circonstance qui a lieu constamment dans toutes les réductions métalliques me conduisit à faire quelques recherches sur cet objet: je remarquai que, dans toutes ces opérations, il y avait une effervescence considérable au moment où le métal passait de l'état de chaux à l'état métallique; il etait naturel d'en conclure qu'il se dégageait un gaz, et j'imaginai un appareil propre à le rassembler et à le recueillir.[35]

This revealing statement is immediately followed by a reference to the sealed note of November 1, specifically to the first experiments on minium and to the great quantity of air released when the lead calx was reduced. But it must refer to the period of his first speculations on effervescences, for the apparatus he refers to is precisely that mentioned in the August memorandum.

How his attention was attracted to this phenomenon is clear from a similar reference in his *Opuscules physiques et chimiques* of 1774. Here he remarks that when he began to suspect that atmospheric air was capable of being fixed in metals, he saw that its addition would explain "les phénomènes de la calcination, l'augmentation de poids de métaux convertis en chaux, et peut-être beaucoup d'autres phénomènes dont les physiciens n'avaient encore donné aucune explication satisfaisante." Three facts lent credibility to this hypothesis: first, that calcination cannot take place in closed vessels from which air is excluded; second, that the greater the surface of the metal exposed

---

[35] *Oeuvres de Lavoisier,* II, 628.

to the air, the more readily calcination takes place; and third a fact "reconnu de tous les métallurgistes, et observé par tous ceux qui ont travaillé aux opérations de docimasie, que, dans toute réduction, il y a effervescence au moment où la substance métallique passe de l'état de chaux à celui de métal; or une effervescence n'est communément autre chose qu'un dégagement de fluide élastique sous forme fixe, qui reprend son élasticité au moment de la réduction." [36] Though not intended as an exact historical account—indeed, for the sake of presenting his results in the *Opuscules* in logical fashion, Lavoisier rather confuses the order of events—this adds support to the specific statement he made later that it was the phenomenon of effervescence observed in the reduction of metals which pointed the way to his great series of experiments.

Lavoisier may well have observed this phenomenon himself in the course of his chemical and mineralogical investigations; yet there is nothing in his early work to suggest that he had acquired any close familiarity with problems of metallurgy and assaying. Since he describes the phenomenon as familiar to all metallurgists and assayers, it was probably from his reading that he was led to a knowledge of this effect. Moreover, he speaks of these effervescences as observed in all reductions; but this

[36] *Ibid.*, I, 598. Lavoisier's introductory remarks suggest that the experiments listed in the preceding chapter of the *Opuscules*—on the increased weight of metallic precipitates from solution—were actually performed *before* his speculations on the increased weight of calcined metals. This is not the case; the experiments by the wet way date from the spring and summer of 1773, as Lavoisier's *registres* make clear. See Berthelot, *op. cit.*, pp. 238–239 and 247.

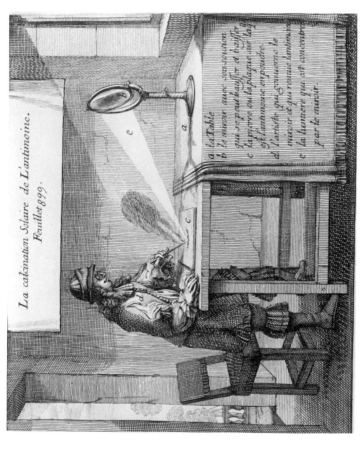

La calcination Solaire de L'antimoine.
Feuillet 899.

a la Table
b le miroir avec son soutien
qui se peut hausser et baisser
à le서 ou à la plaque sur la q
que l'antimoine expose
d l'Artiste qui gouverne le
miroir et qui remue l'antimoine
e la lumiere qui est concentrée
par le miroir.

1. The solar calcination of antimony according to Nicolas Le Fèvre, 1660
(Duveen collection–University of Wisconsin)

né en 1677 HALES. mort en 1761

2. A French portrait engraving of Stephen Hales, 1677–1761
(Photographie L. Le Charles)

LOUIS BERNARD GUYTON-MORVEAU.

Né a Dijon le 4 Janvier 1737.

N-94. Dessiné et Gravé au Physionotrace par Quenedey, rue Croix des Petits Champs, N°.20. à Paris.

3. Louis Bernard Guyton de Morveau, 1737–1816 (Author's collection)

4. Jean Charles Philibert Trudaine de Montigny, 1733–1777 (Bibliothèque Nationale)

5. Anne Robert Jacques Turgot, 1721–1781 (Bibliothèque Nationale)

PETRUS-JOSEPHUS MACQUER.
Doctor Medicus Parisiensis, Censor regius, regiæ Societatis
Taurinensis, regiæ academiæ Stockolmiensis, regiæ scientiarum
academiæ socius et in horto regio Chymiæ Professor à rege
designatus et nominatus.

JB. Garrand pinx. *Observabat Josephus-Thomas-Philippus Henry Duparc in utroque Jure Licenciatus.* *G. Benard Sculp.*

6. Pierre Joseph Macquer, 1718–1784 (Bibliothèque Nationale)

L'ABBÉ ROZIER.

Le vrai seul fut son but.

7. François Rozier, 1734–1793 (Bibliothèque Nationale)

9. Balthazar Georges Sage, 1740–1824
(Author's collection)

8. Antoine Baumé, 1728–1804
(Bibliothèque Nationale)

11. N. J. von Jacquin, 1727–1817, the chief Continental disciple of Joseph Black (Author's collection)

10. Nicholas Desmarest, 1725–1815 (Author's collection)

effect is most striking, and was probably most familiar, in the case of the calx or ores of lead. This, indeed, was the instance singled out by the authors—and by no means all metallurgical writers refer to this effect—who may have influenced Lavoisier. The *locus classicus* is probably the clear description in J. A. Cramer's *Elementa artis doci-masticae* (1730), a standard work on assaying, known and cited by French chemists even before its appearance in French in 1755. I give the passage from the French translation Lavoisier may have seen; here, speaking of the reduction of lead ores, Cramer writes:

Il est bon d'observer que le feu doit être modéré pendant quelque tems au commencement de l'opération, parce que la matiere se raréfie prodigieusement pendant la réduction du plomb. On peut s'en convaincre en jettant de la poudre de charbons sur de la litharge en fonte dans un test placé sous la moufle; car pour-lors le bain perd sa tranquillité. Ce phénomene arrive pour la moindre quantité de phlogistique: en sorte que l'on fait rarement fondre de la litharge sans qu'elle bouillonne & écume avec sifflement. Ainsi donc si l'on vient à augmenter le feu trop rapidement, la mine calcinée & mêlée exactement avec le flux salin charbonneux perce le lut, & la plus grande partie du plomb se trouve dispersée par grains ou hors du vaisseau, ou au dedans, étant appliquée aux endroits qui sont audessus du flux. On évite cet inconvénient en donnant un degré de feu modéré jusqu'à ce que la réduction soit finie: ce qu'on connôit par la cessation du bouillonnement qui arrive encore pour-lors; pourvu toutefois qu'il ne soit pas dû à l'humidité du flux.[37]

[37] *Elémens de docimastique, ou de l'art des essais* (Paris, 1755), III, 336–337. Lavoisier owned the second Latin edition of this work.

Lavoisier may well have known this passage in Cramer's work, for it was frequently noted by French chemists. But he did not have to know this important metallurgical work at first hand to have encountered clear descriptions of the phenomenon, because Macquer made considerable use of the original Latin version of Cramer's book in writing his *Elémens de chymie pratique* (1751) and had at hand the French translation when he produced his second edition in 1756. The effervescence of lead ores on reduction is described by Macquer almost in the words of Cramer's translator:

Il est important de ne donner dans le commencement qu'un degré de chaleur modéré, parceque quand la terre de Plomb se combine avec le phlogistique pour prendre la forme métallique, elle se gonfle de telle sorte, qu'il est à craindre que toute la matiere ne sorte des vases qui la contiennent. C'est aussi pour éviter cet inconvénient, que nous avons prescrit de se servir d'un très-grand creuset. Ce gonflement qui arrive au Plomb lors de sa réduction, est accompagné d'un bruit semblable à un sifflement d'air.[38]

This caution is repeated farther on, and Macquer adds that it is necessary when melting the glass of lead to keep the crucible tightly sealed to prevent charcoal, "ou autre matière inflammable," from falling in,

[38] P. J. Macquer, *Elémens de chymie-pratique* (2nd ed.; Paris, 1756), I, 297. Macquer makes a brief reference to this phenomenon in his *Dictionnaire de chymie* (ed. 1766), II, 367, art. "Réduction ou Révivification," where he cautions the reader to "ménager le feu dans le commencement, pour éviter le trop grand gonflement qu'occasionne ordinairement la réaction du principe inflammable sur les terres métalliques."

car quand cela arrive, il se fait une réduction du Plomb, qui est toujours accompagnée d'une espece d'effervescence, & d'un boursoufflement si considérable, qu'ordinairement la plus grande partie du mêlange se répand hors du creuset.[39]

This striking behavior of the calx of lead is a good example of what Francis Bacon called *shining* or *predominant instances* "which exhibit the nature in question naked and standing by itself, and also in its exhaltation or highest degree of power."[40] It had aroused the interest of at least one other chemist of Lavoisier's circle, Balthazar-Georges Sage (1740–1824), just at the time when the first interest in pneumatic chemistry was being awakened in France. A somewhat younger man than Lavoisier and a pharmacist with a strong interest in mineralogy, Sage had been an *adjoint chimiste* of the Academy since September, 1770. Early in 1772 he published his *Elémens de minéralogie docimastique*, a chemical mineralogy which described, often vaguely and inaccurately, the principal substances of metallurgical interest.[41] Sage did not discuss, as did Cramer, the actual processes of the metallurgist or the assayer, so he had no occasion to

[39] *Ibid.*, p. 314. These passages from Macquer were drawn to my attention by Dr. Cyril Stanley Smith of the University of Chicago. Baron, who frequently cites Cramer in his notes to Lémery (1756), says all who have written on metals since Cramer have been content to "transcrire mot pour mot les procédés & les judicieuses Réflexions de cet excellent Auteur." See p. 125, note b.

[40] *The Philosophical Works of Francis Bacon*, ed. John M. Robertson (London, 1905), p. 329.

[41] This book, which Meldrum believed to have exerted an influence upon Lavoisier, appeared early in 1772. The *privilège* is dated December 18, 1771. It was reviewed in the April issue of Rozier's journal.

refer to the phenomenon of effervescences during the reduction of ores or calxes. Yet Sage was certainly familiar
with the effect Cramer described, for late in the fall of
1772 he planned to investigate this very phenomenon,
unaware that Lavoisier had forestalled him. In this experiment, designed in co-operation with Condorcet, the
calx of lead was to be heated with charcoal "dans une
cornue dont le bout lutté sera garni d'un tube plongé
dans l'eau de chaux." If when the calx is reduced, the limewater should be precipitated, this would be an indication
that the reduction or "rephlogistication" of the lead had
produced "ce que nous appelons air fixe." [42] I cannot
find that this experiment was ever performed, but at all
events its conception was doubtless wholly independent of
Lavoisier and it must have been carried out later than the
famous experiment Lavoisier performed on the same or a
closely similar substance. As we shall see, the possibility
that the calx of metals contained air was perhaps suggested
by Condorcet as a result of an interesting exchange of
letters with Turgot to be described below.[43] But it must
have been Sage, with his knowledge of chemistry and
metallurgical processes, who thought of reducing the
oxide of lead; he was doubtless familiar with the same
phenomenon of effervescence on reduction which Lavoisier tells us first aroused his own curiosity.

[42] *Correspondance inédite de Condorcet et de Turgot, 1770–
1779, publiée avec des notes et une introduction d'après les auto-
graphes de la collection Minoret et les manuscrits de l'Institut, par
M. Charles Henry* (Paris, 1883), p. 108.

[43] See below, Chapter V.

CHAPTER 4

The Mysterious Calcination

of Metals

IF, for the various reasons we have advanced, Lavoisier came to suspect, in the summer of 1772, that air is given off when metallic calxes are reduced, and consequently that it is absorbed when metals are burned or roasted, he had also become aware, at about the same time, of the significant fact that some metals, perhaps all metals that can be burned, gain weight when they are calcined. Here was a phenomenon which the phlogiston theory could not adequately explain; for, according to this widely held theory, burning and calcination were accompanied by a *loss* of this hypothetical fire principle, whereas an increase in weight should prove that something had been added. This *fait capital*, as Lavoisier later called it—that the calx of a metal is heavier than the regulus—we know to have been of crucial importance in the crystallization of his thought. He mentioned it in the sealed note of November; and in the *Opuscules* of 1774 he singled it out as of real importance, as we have seen above. Later still, in his "Réflexions sur le phlogistique," he emphasized the point strongly:

111

Suivant Stahl, le phlogistique, le principe inflammable, est un corps pesant; et, en effet, on ne peut pas se former une autre idée d'un principe terreux, ou au moins dans la composition duquel entre l'élément terreux; il a même essayé, dans son traité du soufre, d'en déterminer la pesanteur.

Cette théorie de Stahl sur la calcination des métaux et sur la combustion en général ne rendait pas compte d'un phénomène très-anciennement observé, vérifié par Boyle, *et qui est devenu aujourd'hui une vérité incontestable,* c'est que tous les corps combustibles augmentent de poids pendant le temps qu'ils brûlent et se calcinent . . . Or, dans le système de Stahl, il s'échappe des métaux, pendant qu'on les calcine, et des corps combustibles qui brûlent, du phlogistique qui est un principe pesant; ils doivent donc perdre une quantité de leur poids au lieu d'en acquérir.[1]

Historians have never doubted the influence of the augmentation effect on Lavoisier's thought and have been well aware of the use he made of it in arguing against the phlogiston theory. But I believe he did not merely think of this later, when seeking to refute the phlogistonists; for, as the reference in the *Opuscules* suggests, it supplied one of the most significant facts that led him, in the first instance, to suspect the participation of air in the transformation of metals.

But there is a further point worth stressing. Historians of chemistry seem always to have assumed that this *fait capital,* the augmentation of the calx, was a familiar fact which had been known for well over a century and that it had been widely accepted. Only the blind stubbornness of the adherents of the phlogiston theory, so runs this interpretation, prevented these early chemists from seeing

[1] *Oeuvres de Lavoisier,* II, 625–626. The italics are mine.

how fatal to their cherished theory was this single, well-established fact; it was therefore left to the genius of Lavoisier, with his rigorously gravimetric approach to chemistry, to perceive its significance. The matter is not quite so simple as historians of science have believed. Surprisingly enough, when Lavoisier began his study of chemistry, this *fait capital* had not been firmly established and was far from being generally accepted. It was only proved to everyone's satisfaction by experiments performed, not long before the period we are discussing, by Lavoisier's future disciple, the Dijon lawyer and amateur chemist, Louis-Bernard Guyton de Morveau (1737–1816), a man whom Lavoisier at this time had not yet met but whose work he certainly knew. Guyton's experiments, probably carried out in 1770, first came to the attention of the scientists of Paris in the years 1771–1772, with consequences that scholars have not fully appreciated. Moreover, the results Guyton obtained, and which proved the augmentation effect beyond a doubt, came to general notice at precisely the moment when the possible role of air in chemical change was beginning to occupy the attention of French chemists.

The Augmentation of the Calx

It had, of course, long been known that lead—which is readily calcined—increases markedly in weight when by being strongly heated it is transformed into minium (red lead) or litharge; this fact had been frequently noted as early as the sixteenth century.[2] The augmentation effect

[2] J. H. White, *The History of the Phlogiston Theory* (London, 1932), pp. 33 ff., has a general treatment of the augmentation problem. See also J. R. Partington and Douglas McKie, "Historical

soon came to be almost as well known in the case of tin, as we learned from the famous—indeed unwarrantedly famous—*Essays* of Jean Rey (1630).[3] During the seventeenth century this striking phenomenon was reported for a number of other metals; in particular, the so-called "solar calcination" of antimony attracted widespread attention after several writers recorded that when this metal is calcined by the heat of a burning glass its weight increases markedly. This seems to have been first reported in the *Basilica antimonii* of Hamerus Poppius (1618), an author cited by Rey; [4] but the most influential account of this solar calcination of antimony was given in 1660 by Nicolas Lefèvre (or Lefebvre) in his *Traicté de chymie,* a work which was soon translated into English and which evoked considerable interest in the circle of the Royal Society of London.[5] Not long after, Otto Tachenius in his

Studies of the Phlogiston Theory—I. The Levity of Phlogiston," *Annals of Science*, 2 (1937), 361–373. A valuable bibliography is given in Crell's *Chemische Annalen*, I (1795), 287–289 and notes.

[3] A facsimile edition of this excessively rare work has been published, with a valuable introduction, by Douglas McKie, *The Essays of Jean Rey. A Facsimile Reprint of the Original Edition of 1630* (London, 1951). See also the English version, *Essays of Jean Rey, Doctor of Medicine, On an Enquiry into the Cause Wherefore Tin and Lead Increase in Weight on Calcination (1630)* (Alembic Club Reprints, no. 11; Edinburgh, 1895).

[4] On Poppius see Kopp, *op. cit.*, III (1845), 120.

[5] This translation appeared shortly after Lefèvre arrived in England to serve Charles II as royal apothecary and professor of chemistry. It was dedicated to the king, under the title: *A Compleat Body of Chymistry . . . by Nicasius le Febure, Royal Professor in Chymistry to his Majesty of England, and Apothecary in Ordinary to His Honorable Household. Rendred into English by P. D. C. Esq. one of the Gentlemen of his Majesties Privy Chamber* (London, 1664). Lefèvre's arrival in England and the appearance of the trans-

Hippocrates chimicus (1666) reported the successful calcination of antimony in a "Glass-mens oven, or Furnace," noting the augmentation and the fact that the original weight could be recovered upon reduction.[6]

In Paris the solar calcination of antimony was confirmed about 1667 by Samuel Cottereau, Sieur Du Clos, one of the founding members of the Académie royale des sciences, who also reported the increase in weight of other metals—lead, tin, iron, and copper—during their conversion into calxes.[7] Even more persuasive evidence for the generality of the phenomenon of augmentation was supplied by the experiments of the great Robert Boyle. In his *Essays of Effluviums* (1673) he showed—by heating bits of metal in open crucibles over a sulphur flame and in a cupellation furnace—that an increase in weight could be detected in calcined copper, tin, lead, steel filings, zinc or spelter filings, and tutenag.[8] To the list of sub-

---

lation of his book stimulated an interest in these problems on the part of members of the Royal Society like Jonathan Goddard and Robert Boyle. See Thomas Birch, *History of the Royal Society* (London, 1756–1757), I, 19–20, 445, 452. A good account of Lefèvre is given in John Read, *Humour and Humanism in Chemistry* (London, 1947), pp. 101–114.

[6] This work and his *Hippocraticae medicinae clavis manuali experientia in naturae fontibus elaborata,* etc. (1669) were published together in English as *Otto Tachenius. his Hippocrates Chymicus . . . with his Clavis thereunto. Translated by J. W.* (London, 1677). See especially this translation, p. 62.

[7] For these experiments see J. B. Duhamel, *Regiae scientiarum academiae historia* (Paris, 1698), pp. 13–14. On Du Clos see the sketch by Condorcet in *Oeuvres de Condorcet,* ed. A. Condorcet O'Connor and F. Arago; II, 38–39. According to Homberg, Du Clos calcined antimony using "un des miroirs ardens de l'observatoire." See *Mém. Acad. roy. sci.* for 1705 (1706), p. 94.

[8] "New Experiments to Make Fire and Flame Ponderable," in

stances studied by Boyle there was soon added mercury. Wilhelm (or Guillaume) Homberg (1652–1715), a chemist of the Academy of Sciences, successfully confirmed the solar calcination of antimony, using the great Tschirnhausen lens acquired by the Duc d'Orléans, and in the paper in which he described these results he recorded that when mercury is converted into a red powder by long heating the powder becomes heavier than the metal.[9]

Thus by the end of the seventeenth century there was little reason for chemists to doubt the reality of the augmentation effect in the calcination of a number of different metals. Whereas Nicolas Lémery, in his influential *Cours de chymie* (1675), mentioned the increase in weight of lead and the regulus of antimony, and in later editions of this work added a reference to tin,[10] other writers did not hesitate to assert the generality of the phenomenon. Among these were the Newtonian chemist, John Freind, in his *Praelectiones chymicae* (1709) [11] and the great

---

The Works of the Honourable Robert Boyle, III, 341–346. For a summary of these experiments see Marie Boas, *Robert Boyle and Seventeenth Century Chemistry* (Cambridge, 1958), pp. 198–200; and Douglas McKie in *Science Progress,* 29 (1934), 253 f.

[9] *Mém. Acad. roy. sci.* for 1705 (1706), pp. 92–94. Louis Lémery (1677–1743), who advanced a theory similar to Homberg's and attributed the gain in weight of calcined metals to the addition of "matière de lumière," states that the effect is generally recognized for the regulus of antimony, lead, tin, and even mercury. See his "Conjectures et réflexions sur la matière du feu ou de la lumière," *Mém. Acad. roy. sci.* for 1709 (1711), pp. 400–418.

[10] See Nicolas Lémery, *Cours de chymie* (5th ed.; Paris, 1683), pp. 119–120 and 225. This edition still is silent on the augmentation of tin, but see the edition of 1756 described below, pp. 122–123, where the new paragraph on tin is found on p. 95.

[11] John Freind, *Praelectiones chymicae* (3rd ed.; Leyden, 1734), p. 12. The English version reads: "So *Lead,* and all other *Metals,*

pundit of the phlogiston theory, Georg Ernst Stahl, whose opinion was echoed by his disciples.[12]

The earliest explanation given of this mysterious phenomenon—mysterious because, as Biringuccio remarked, it is the nature of fire "to consume everything with a diminution of substances"[13]—was that it was caused by the removal of some lighter constituent, air or celestial heat. This early view, advanced with individual variations by Biringuccio, Cardan, and Scaliger, was not popular in the seventeenth century, though Cardan's version of the theory is echoed by Kunckel.[14] It was most generally assumed, before the advent of the phlogiston theory, that the augmentation must be due to the addition of some

---

gain in their weight by Calcination: for if an *Ounce* of *Lead* be reduc'd to a Calx, by the *Flame* of *Spirit* of *Wine,* it will increase above a Scruple in weight" (*Chymical Lectures* [2nd ed.; London, 1729], p. 25).

[12] *Zufällige Gedancken und nützliche Bedencken über den Streit von dem sogenannten Sulphure,* etc. (Halle, 1718), p. 329; Partington and McKie (*loc. cit.,* p. 369, note 16) give the crucial lines. I have also used d'Holbach's translation (*Traité du soufre* [Paris, 1766]), where we read: "car dans les metaux inflammables elle [phlogiston] produit un effet très-opposé, puisque leurs chaux deviennent plus pesantes, & redeviennent plus légeres par son addition" (p. 277). Elsewhere it is less evident that Stahl believed in the generality of the phenomenon, for he speaks only of lead, tin, and the regulus of antimony in his *Fundamenta chymiae* (2nd ed.; Nuremberg, 1746–1747), II, 374 and 507–508. But one of Stahl's earliest French disciples, J. B. Senac, wrote: "L'Augmentation des corps calcinez prouve que les parties se divisent & s'éloignent les unes des autres." See *Nouveau cours de chymie, suivant les principes de Newton & de Sthall* (2nd ed.; Paris, 1737), I, 160.

[13] *The Pirotechnica of Vannochio Biringuccio,* trans. by Cyril Stanley Smith and Martha Teach Gnudi (New York, 1943), pp. 58–59.

[14] Partington and McKie, *loc. cit.,* pp. 369–370.

external substance possessing weight. Today the most often cited explanation is the one that Jean Rey gave in his *Essays*—that the augmentation is due to the addition of air to the metal. But Rey's opinion has frequently been misinterpreted. His explanation is physical rather than chemical, for what he describes is the adherence of air to the calx that the fire has already produced in some unspecified manner; just as, he says, wet sand is heavier because the water moistens and adheres to the grains. Rey's theory did not attract much attention, but it may not have been as totally ignored by chemists in the seventeenth century as historians generally believe.[15] Nevertheless, the most popular theory was that which ascribed the augmentation to the fixation of *corpuscules ignés*, i.e., of ponderable particles of fire or light. This was the view put forth in the writings of Nicolas Lémery, Otto Tachenius, Moïse Charas, and Robert Boyle. John Mayow, for his part, combined this with his favorite theory of an aerial niter and attributed the increase in weight of calcined antimony to the nitroaerial and igneous particles

[15] Birch records that when Dr. Goddard reported to the Royal Society in July, 1664, that he had found antimony to decrease in weight when exposed to a burning glass instead of increasing, "Mr. Boyle affirm'd, that he had like success in such an experiment; but that Monsieur Le Febure, who asserted the increase of antimony calcined by the sun, hearing of such success with him, answered, that it had not been calcined enough to reduce to a fixed salt for the imbibing of air" (Birch, *History of the Royal Society of London*, I, 452). See also Tachenius' *Clavis* where the author attacks the notion that the increase in weight of lead can be due to air. He does not mention Rey but attributes this theory (as the English version gives it) to "Deans with their Fellows" and to "your Doctorships." See *Otto Tachenius. his Hippocrates Chymicus*, p. 62.

fixed in it by the solar rays of the burning glass.[16] Somewhat similar was the view of Du Clos, who imagined that the gain in weight came from impurities or sulphurous particles in the air.

Yet despite all this evidence there was by no means unanimity that the augmentation effect was invariably encountered or that it was really significant. Simon Boulduc (1652–1729), a chemist of the early Academy of Sciences, reported that antimony lost weight when calcined in an open vessel; [17] and John Francis Vigani, the Italian scientist who briefly assisted Newton in his chemical experiments, announced in his *Medulla chymiae* (1693) that when he calcined antimony with a burning glass he found a loss of weight, and he insisted that those who claimed the contrary were in error.[18] Early in the eighteenth century Nicolas Hartsoeker (1656–1725) carried out experiments which convinced him that calcination with the burning glass could produce no increase in weight of lead, tin, or other metals.[19]

Even those persons, and they were well in the majority, who did not doubt that lead, tin, and antimony showed the augmentation effect, were far from sure that the

[16] *Tractatus quinque medico-physici* (Oxford, 1674), pp. 28–29. Cf. John Mayow, *Medico-Physical Works* (Edinburgh and Chicago, 1908), pp. 20–21.

[17] Duhamel, *op. cit.*, p .14, where we read: "Nam D. Bouleduc nuper in Academia testatus est antimonium crudum in vase fictili calcinatem pondere imminutum fuisse."

[18] Vigani's views are cited by Baron in his edition of Lémery's *Cours de chymie* (Paris, 1756), p. 268, note h.

[19] Douglas McKie, "Béraut's Theory of Calcination (1747)," *Annals of Science*, 1 (1936), 272 and note 15.

effect was chemically significant and thought it might result from the addition of impurities. This, indeed, had been suggested by Caesalpinus in the sixteenth century. But it was Hermann Boerhaave who most effectively confused the issue. Having shown in a famous experiment that an iron bar weighed no more when it was heated than when it was cold, he concluded that heat or the matter of fire is destitute of weight. The augmentation effect could hardly, then, be attributed to igneous corpuscles, as so many had believed, or to the particles of fire or light. That an increase in weight could be observed in the case of bodies "abounding in a rapacious sulphur, as antimony, lead, tin, iron, and orpiment," he did not deny; yet he was inclined to ascribe it to the "acid of the fewel" imbibed by the metal or to particles communicated from glass or earthen vessels or from the iron ladles with which the melt was sometimes stirred.[20]

Boerhaave's great influence and authority served to encourage doubts that the augmentation phenomenon was general and seemed to deflate its significance. When Voltaire, early in 1737, resolved to compete for the prize offered by the Academy of Sciences for the best essay on the nature of heat, he requested a correspondent in Paris to send him Boerhaave's *Chemistry*, to find out the opinion of the chemists Geoffroy and Grosse concerning the experiments of Lémery the younger and Homberg, and

[20] Shaw-Boerhaave (1741), I, 339–340. Boerhaave cites the experiments of Boyle, Du Clos, and Homberg in support of the role of igneous particles but remarks that the experiments of Boulduc strongly favor the contrary opinion. It would seem that Boerhaave first accepted the theory of igneous particles but that his experiment on the iron bar shook his confidence. Cf. P. Shaw and E. Chambers, *New Method of Chemistry*, I, 79.

to learn whether they believed Homberg's experiments on calcination more worthy of credence than Boerhaave's on the iron bar.[21] This apparent contradiction still troubled Voltaire when he produced his *Essai sur la nature du feu* (1740), although he ended by taking the position that the calcination experiments proved that fire has weight.[22]

The same problem was treated by Mme du Châtelet, Voltaire's friend, mistress, and scientific associate. In her *Dissertation sur la nature et la propagation du feu* (1744) she contrasts the positive results of Boyle and Homberg with the negative ones of Boulduc and Hartsoeker, and she notes the hesitations of Boerhaave. She concludes, unlike Voltaire, that fire is very nearly weightless and that the weight increase in calcination experiments must be due to the intrusion of extraneous matter.[23]

The French chemists shared these doubts. Venel's article on calcination in Diderot's *Encyclopédie* makes only the cautious statement that "certain metallic substances" show the augmentation effect and that this effect is especially remarkable in the case of lead.[24] P. J. Macquer, who had stated in his *Elémens de chymie pratique* (1751) that the calxes of the imperfect metals, notably lead, increase in weight on calcination,[25] significantly omitted any such

[21] Voltaire, *Oeuvres,* ed. Moland, XXXIV, 253, 277, 285, 292.

[22] *Essai sur la nature du feu, et sur sa propagation* (Paris, 1740). See also *Oeuvres,* ed. Moland, XXII, 279–325.

[23] *Dissertation sur la nature et la propagation du feu* (Paris, 1744), pp. 23–34.

[24] *Encyclopédie,* II (1751), art. "Calcination."

[25] P. J. Macquer, *Elémens de chymie pratique* (Paris, 1751), I, 309–310. Macquer is distinctly cautious about this "singular phenomenon." Many theories have been advanced to explain it, but none have proved satisfactory, so he proposes to offer none. See also

statement from the first edition of his *Dictionnaire de chymie* (1766). If the influence of Boerhaave cannot be demonstrated in the case of Macquer, it is clearly evident in the case of his younger disciple, Antoine Baumé (1728–1804), who gives a summary of Boerhaave's discussion of the calcination problem and agrees with Boerhaave that "on n'a pas pris sur cette matière toutes les précautions convenables pour s'assurer de la cause de cette augmentation." [26] More significant still, the elder Rouelle evidently did not consider the weight effect worthy of serious attention; when he discusses the calcination of lead and tin he makes no reference to the augmentation of the calx, and in the section of his lectures that treats of antimony he insists that the increase in weight of the calx is only apparent and is due to the greater density of the calx.[27] This theory, put forward by Juncker and derived by him from Kunckel, enjoyed considerable popularity in the eighteenth century.[28]

The prevailing hesitation and confusion was clearly summed up by the chemist and physician, Théodore Baron (1715–1768), in the new edition of Lémery's *Cours de chymie,* which he published in 1756. To Lémery's discussion of the calcination of lead, Baron appends a long note in which Robert Boyle is credited with having been the

Elements of the Theory and Practice of Chemistry, translated from the French of M. Macquer (London, 1758), I, 388–389.

[26] A. Baumé, *Manuel de chimie* (Paris, 1763), pp. 31–32. On Baumé see Balteau, *op. cit.,* V (1951), 934–935.

[27] "Cours de chymie de Mr Rouelle," Bordeaux MS, pp. 970 and 1031–1032.

[28] For a discussion of this theory see Metzger, *Newton, Stahl, Boerhaave,* pp. 187–188; and Partington and McKie, *loc. cit.,* pp. 369–370.

first to speak of "cette augmentation de poids qui arrive aux matieres métalliques par la calcination." Boyle's results were confirmed by the experiments of Homberg and Lémery the younger, and their doctrine "est aujourd'hui celui du plus grand nombre des Physiciens." But Boerhaave, it is pointed out, had raised some serious difficulties, and Baron proceeds to enumerate them almost exactly as Boerhaave himself did, stressing that the weight effect was probably due to impurities, even in Boyle's experiments in closed vessels where particles of glass may have been picked up by the metal. Moreover, he emphasized, not all metals show this increase in weight, and he concludes: "Il suit de tout ce qui vient d'être dit, que le plus sage parti est de suspendre son jugement, jusqu'à ce que de nouvelles expériences nous ayent fourni de nouveaux éclaircissemens." [29]

Much stronger opposition was expressed by two German chemists. Rudolph Augustin Vogel (1724–1774), a versatile if second-rank scientist and physician of Göttingen, published in 1753 a brief Latin paper in which he sought to review the whole question.[30] After a valuable survey of what had been written on the subject, he concluded from the evidence of his own experiments that only lead shows the augmentation effect; other metals, he thought, fell into two groups: a small one, which included tin and copper, showed no change in weight on calcina-

[29] Page 113, note a.
[30] *Experimenta chemicorum de incremento ponderis corporum quorundam igne calcinatorum examinat* (Göttingen, n.d. [1753]). I have not seen the original, the title of which I have given from Bolton, but have used the edition with a slightly different title in *Rudolphi Augustini Vogel Opuscula Medica Selecta* (Göttingen, 1768), pp. 53–68.

tion; a much larger group, including zinc and antimony, displayed a small decrease.

Much the same conclusion was reached a decade later by the Alsatian chemist, apothecary, and physician, Jacob Reinbold Spielmann (1722–1783), a man best remembered as Goethe's chemistry teacher during the Strasbourg days.[31] Spielmann's *Institutiones chemiae* appeared in 1763, with a second edition in 1766; a French translation by Cadet de Gassicourt (Lavoisier's collaborator in the diamond experiments) was published four years later. Even French chemists whose Latin was weak or wanting could now readily learn that Spielmann refused to admit any increase in weight when metals are calcined, except in the case of lead:

On a observé que . . . la calcination ne faisoit qu'augmenter le poids du plomb; phénomène que de grands artistes ont observé relativement à d'autres fossiles. Mais, sur ce dernier point, ils éprouvent des contradictions de la part de quelques auteurs célèbres. Je suis, d'après mes Expériences, fondé à etre de l'avis de ces derniers.[32]

From the evidence given above we can readily understand how Guyton de Morveau could write in 1772 that, while nobody doubted that lead gains about 10 per cent

[31] On Spielmann see Ferguson, *op. cit.*, II, 394. Spielmann's *Institutiones* was one of the books bought by Lavoisier from König, the Strasbourg bookseller, on the occasion of the famous mineralogical trip to the Vosges in 1767. See *Oeuvres de Lavoisier—Correspondance*, I (1955), 98.

[32] *Instituts de chymie de M. Jacques-Reinbold-Spielmann. Traduits du latin, sur la seconde Edition, par M. Cadet le jeune* (Paris, 1770), II, 119–120. This passage was later cited, but somewhat inaccurately, by Guyton de Morveau.

in weight when it is calcined, it was by no means clear what happened with other metallic calxes: "Les Auteurs sont en quelque sorte partagés sur ce fait." [33]

The Experiments of Guyton de Morveau

Louis-Bernard Guyton de Morveau (1737–1816), a man six years Lavoisier's senior, was already by 1772 esteemed in his native Dijon as a lawyer of ability, a writer of some local reputation, and a member of that city's scientific and literary academy. If known at all outside his Burgundian province, it could only have been for his literary, rather than any scientific, achievements, especially perhaps for his *Mémoire sur l'éducation publique,* a plea for free, public, secular education, which he published in 1764 and which was even translated into Spanish. It was inspired, like the similar but better-known work of La Chalotais, by the suppression of the Jesuit order and the ensuing crisis in French education.[34]

Guyton was thirty before he entered seriously on a scientific career,[35] although he seems to have begun some

[33] *Digressions académiques,* pp. 7–8. For a discussion of this book see below, note 47. I have not seen N. A. Becher, *De igne & gravitate calcis metallicae* (Ingolstadt, 1772), cited in Crell, *loc. cit.,* or J. A. Carl's *De igne et gravitate calcis metallicae* (Ingolstadt, 1772), mentioned by Crell and in Gmelin, *Geschichte der Chemie,* III, 475. Neither work appeared in time to influence Guyton.

[34] He had also published an *Eloge du président Jeannin* (Paris, 1766) and some legal discourses.

[35] On Guyton de Morveau see Georges Bouchard, *Guyton-Morveau, chimiste et conventionnel (1737–1816)* (Paris, 1938). This can still be supplemented on a number of points by A. B. Granville, "An Account of the Life and Writings of Baron Guyton de Morveau," *Journal of Science and the Arts,* 3 (1817), 249–296, a work that also appeared separately (in-8°, London, 1817).

years earlier to teach himself chemistry out of Macquer's books and Baumé's *Manuel de chimie* (1763). From Baumé, who sold pharmaceuticals and chemical supplies in Paris and had what was almost a small factory, Guyton ordered reagents and chemical apparatus; and by 1768 he began equipping in his home that impressive laboratory and mineralogical cabinet which later evoked the admiration of Arthur Young. It was perhaps in July of that year that Guyton first met Macquer and Baumé on a trip to Paris "for the purpose of visiting the scientific establishments of that metropolis, and purchasing books, preparations, and instruments, which he still wanted to enable him to pursue his favorite study." [36]

Guyton's first scientific paper of importance, his "Mémoire sur les phénomènes de l'air dans la combustion," was read before the Academy of Dijon on December 11, 1768. The topic is significant, and so was Guyton's approach to it; together they reveal once again how all-pervasive the influence of Stephen Hales had come to be, for Guyton tried to show, in opposition to Hales, that air was not consumed when substances burn and that its role in combustion, as nearly everybody believed, is purely mechanical.[37]

[36] Granville, *loc. cit.*, p. 259.

[37] *Mémoires de l'Académie des sciences, arts et belles-lettres de Dijon,* I (1769), 416–436. A summary of Guyton's paper appeared in the *Mercure de France* for August, 1769, pp. 150–156. The *Mercure* account says that Guyton presented this paper on December 11, 1768, in the lecture room of the university. But Bouchard (*op. cit.*, pp. 52 and 77) gives the date as January 8, 1768, and records a somewhat different title: "Dissertation sur l'action de l'air dans la combustion des corps." The title I have adopted is that found in the Dijon *Mémoires* and echoed in the *Mercure*. Guyton later admitted the manipulative defects involved in these early experiments. See

A well-publicized controversy, in which a member of his own Dijon Academy took a leading part, attracted Guyton to the calcination problem. This episode has been carefully studied [38] and needs only to be summarized here. In 1764, at a public session of the Academy, Chardenon, a Dijon physician of whom very little is known,[39] presented a paper entitled "Sur la cause de l'augmentation du poids des substances métalliques calcinées." Without questioning the reality or the generality of the phenomenon of the augmentation of the calx, Chardenon set himself the task of explaining it. He rejected out of hand, as already well enough disproved, the theory that particles of fire become lodged in the metal and make it heavier; but he devotes much space to refuting the theory favored by Du Clos, and elaborated by a certain Père Béraut in 1747, that foreign corpuscles in the air attach themselves to bodies exposed to calcination and in this manner increase their weight. Chardenon's own explanation invoked the phlogiston theory. Phlogiston, he wrote, is nothing but fire; it is characterized by an inherent lightness, a centrifugal tendency toward the outer reaches of

his article "Air" in *Encyclopédie méthodique—Chimie*, 1 (1786), 701.

[38] Partington and McKie, *loc. cit.*, pp. 373–379.

[39] Chardenon, an *agrégé* of the Faculty of Medicine at Dijon, was an *associé* of the Academy in 1744 and became a full member (*pensionnaire*) in 1747. One of the secretaries of the Academy, he had worked with Richard de Ruffey and Claude Gelot in drafting the new statutes of 1762. In all, he made some thirty communications to the Academy. See Ph. Milsand, "Notes et documents pour servir à l'histoire de l'Académie des sciences, arts et belles-lettres de Dijon," in *Mém. Acad. Dijon*, 2nd ser. 16 (1871), 1–29; and Roger Tisserand, *Au Temps de l'Encyclopédie—L'Académie de Dijon de 1740 à 1793* (Vesoul, 1936).

the universe. When combined with a solid, the phlogiston gives "wings to the earthly molecules"; conversely, when the phlogiston is lost during calcination, the metal, deprived of this uplifting force, increases in weight.[40]

An account of Chardenon's paper appeared in the *Mercure de France* in the summer of 1765. This elicited a strong but amiable defense of Père Béraut by an apparently pseudonymous correspondent; it took the form of a letter printed in the *Journal des sçavans* for January, 1768. In it the writer pokes fun at the Dijon doctor's spritely particles, ridicules the idea that a substance can gain weight by losing something and without the addition of new particles, and concludes that "M. Chardenon should have arrayed against him all the astronomers and all the physicists who believe in universal gravitation." [41]

Chardenon replied to this letter by an intemperate

[40] *Mercure de France* for July, 1765 (II, 127–134). As published by the Dijon Academy, Chardenon's paper bore the title "Mémoire sur l'augmentation de poids des métaux calcinés," *Mém. Acad. Dijon*, 1 (1769), 303 f. For the Jesuit Père Béraut (or Béraud) see McKie, "Béraut's Theory of Calcination," *loc. cit.*, 1 (1936), 269–293. For Béraut's relationship to the Academy of Bordeaux, see P. Barrière, *L'Académie de Bordeaux* (Bordeaux and Paris, 1957), *passim*.

[41] *Journal des sçavans*, December, 1767, pp. 889–894. The letter is signed "Ribapotme Prêtre," and is dated Bordeaux, July 20, 1765. Partington and McKie (*loc. cit.*, p. 374, note 35) believe this pseudonymous letter to have been written by Père Béraut himself. This is at least doubtful, for he is referred to in the letter as the "célèbre Professeur de Mathématiques au Collège de Lyon." There is no evidence that Béraut had left Lyons for Bordeaux, though we know he taught at Lyons from 1740 until 1762 when the Jesuit schools were closed. See F. de Dainville, "L'enseignement des mathématiques dans les collèges Jésuites de France du XVIe au XVIIIe siècle (II)," *Revue d'histoire des sciences*, 7 (1954), 115.

address delivered to the Academy of Dijon. We had best draw a veil over this rejoinder, for Chardenon casts doubt upon his antagonist's motives and his devotion to truth and gives anger full reign.[42]

Though he was troubled by Chardenon's fanciful theory, which would necessitate abandoning the accepted principles of physics, Guyton de Morveau nevertheless rallied to his colleague's side in the controversy, discussed the problem with him, and offered to share in research which might clarify matters.[43] He was convinced that the whole question needed careful examination and hoped to be able to salvage the phlogiston theory without abandoning the doctrine of attraction, which, the reader may remember, was to play such a large part in his later system of chemistry. As his modern biographer puts it: "Guyton entreprit donc de justifier Stahl sans attaquer Newton." [44]

Guyton's investigations were probably begun soon after the death of Chardenon, which occurred sometime in 1769, if not while his elder colleague was still alive.[45] At all events, in December, 1770, Guyton presented to the Academy of Dijon a memoir entitled "Dissertation sur le phlogistique considéré comme corps grave et par rapport aux changements de pesanteur qu'il produit sur les

[42] *Journal des sçavans*, September, 1768, pp. 648–658.

[43] "C'est ainsi que j'en ai souvent parlé à M. Chardenon, en lui offrant de partager le travail. Une santé toujours languissante & des occupations trop continues ne lui ont pas permis de s'y livrer; sa mort m'a laissé la tâche toute entière" (*Digressions académiques*, p. 5).

[44] Bouchard, *op. cit.*, p. 154.

[45] It is not unlikely that Guyton's paper of 1768 on the role of air in combustion may have been stimulated by the controversy concerning the role of air in calcination.

corps auxquels il s'unit." [46] This was later published as the first and longest of three essays that together make up Guyton's first scientific book, the *Digressions académiques* (1772).[47] The essay contains some interesting and valuable experimental results as well as Guyton's own phlogistic explanation of the gain in weight of calcined metals.

Guyton's "Dissertation sur le phlogistique," the first essay of the *Digressions,* has been undeservedly neglected by historians of chemistry who, if they mention it at all, ignore the historical and experimental parts and are satisfied to ridicule Guyton's far-fetched theory.[48] Yet it is my

[46] Bouchard, *ibid.*

[47] *Digressions Académiques, ou Essais sur quelques sujets de Physique, de Chymie & d'Histoire naturelle. Par M. Guyton de Morveau, Avocat-Général au Parlement de Dijon, Honoraire de l'Académies des Sciences, Arts & Belles-Lettres de la même Ville, Correspondant de l'Académie Royale des Sciences de Paris. A Dijon, Chez L. N. Frantin,* 1762 [*sic*]. This date is a manifest misprint (for the *approbation* is of March 19, 1772), but it occurs in most copies. W. A. Smeaton reports that two copies, his own and one in the library of the Institut de France, have a corrected title page with the proper date. See his article "L. B. Guyton de Morveau (1737–1816)," *Ambix,* 6 (1957), 18–34. Guyton's book is uncommon; but Smeaton lists six copies in Parisian libraries, one in the Patent Office, London, and one in the library of the University of Edinburgh. In the United States there are copies in the library of the American Philosophical Society, Philadelphia, at Stanford University, and in the private collection of Denis I. Duveen of New York City.

[48] The standard histories of chemistry generally pass over the *Digressions* in silence; Kopp and Hoefer merely cite the title of the book; but Thomas Thomson (*History of Chemistry* [2nd ed.; London, n.d.], II, 179) praises it in general terms. Students of Lavoisier, with the exception of Max Speter, have ignored the book; Maurice Daumas (*Lavoisier* [Paris, 1941], p. 98) mentions it only to remark on the author's "explication du phlogistique toute

contention that Lavoisier owed much to this work, more than he openly acknowledged, for it was Guyton who first proved to the general satisfaction of his contemporaries that all calcinable metals do increase in weight when transformed into their calxes.[49] For this reason—and because of the rarity of the book in which it is published—I feel justified in giving a *précis* of its contents.

The "Dissertation," the only essay of the *Digressions académiques* I shall discuss, is made up of five chapters. The first ("Quelles sont les substances dont le poids augmente réellement par la calcination") is divided into two

---

personelle." Smeaton, in his recent paper (*loc. cit.*, pp. 21–22), alludes to the calcination experiments without comment; he stresses, however, the importance for affinity theory of the "Essai physico-chymique sur la dissolution et la crystallization," which he proposes to analyze in a forthcoming paper.

[49] In only two places have I found Guyton's experiments on calcination given their due. Bouchard (*op. cit.*, p. 154) speaks of Guyton's review of earlier work on the augmentation problem as "un exposé fort érudit," and describes the experimental part of the memoir as "importante et sévèrement conduite." Partington and McKie (*loc. cit.*, p. 389), though chiefly concerned with Guyton's theory of the weight increase, remark that he had "established a fact doubted by many and disputed by others" and call the work "a most notable and historical contribution to chemical literature." They promise detailed consideration of the *Digressions* in a later paper, but this does not seem to have been published; they do not suggest any direct influence of Guyton on Lavoisier, and it is interesting that Douglas McKie makes no mention of the *Digressions* and its possible influence in his *Antoine Lavoisier* (1952). Max Speter alone seems to have suggested that a reading of the *Digressions* may have influenced Lavoisier, but he refers only to the passage where Guyton records the gain in weight of burned phosphorus. See his "Lavoisierana," *Chemiker-Zeitung*, 55 (1931), 994, and below, p. 172.

sections devoted to the history of the augmentation problem; [50] then follow a methodological section ("Principes pour juger & concilier les divers effets des calcinations") [51] and a section of fifteen pages in which he describes his own experiments ("Expériences répétées d'après ces principes").[52] Of the later chapters, devoted to discussing earlier explanations of the phenomenon and to presenting his own theory, I shall say little, because this part of the book has been carefully analyzed by others.[53] It was these later chapters which admittedly created the greatest stir at the time and which—to most modern writers who allude to Guyton's book—have seemed to sum up the importance, or rather the futility, of the entire treatise. Guyton here explains the gain in weight of metals in a manner that seemed to him to reconcile Stahl with Newton: the addition of phlogiston to a metallic calx makes the metal lighter, not because the phlogiston has absolute lightness or "levity," but because it is *specifically* lighter than air. It did not take his contemporaries long to expose the fallacy in his reasoning; yet some at least did not damn the book for these absurdities but perceived the solid qualities to be found elsewhere in it.

The two historical chapters constitute a valuable survey of the literature on the subject; in them Guyton arrays the authorities in favor of the gain in weight of metals against those who denied the effect in whole or in part. But he insists, like the able lawyer he is, that it is not sufficient, when there is conflicting testimony, merely to add more evidence to one side or the other; it is also

[50] *Digressions académiques*, pp. 10–39.   [51] *Ibid.*, pp. 39–71.
[52] *Ibid.*, pp. 72–87.
[53] Partington and McKie, *loc. cit.*, pp. 388–401.

necessary to explain, where possible, the reasons for the divergent testimony of the opposing witnesses.[54] Thus he accounts for Boulduc's claim that antimony lost weight on calcination by pointing out that the earlier chemist had used a crude sample containing a quarter of its weight of common sulphur.[55]

Guyton was at pains to restrict his own investigations to a smaller number of substances than had been customary in such experiments. He discarded as unreliable all claims (like Homberg's) to have calcined the noble metals, with or without change in weight, suggesting that apparently positive results had been due to impurities and loss of weight to mechanical dispersion by the action of fire.[56] He recalled that Robert Boyle claimed to have calcined silver but explained that Boyle had used flaming sulphur as his source of heat and that the fumes of sulphur had probably reacted with the silver.[57] Guyton furthermore discarded all instances of Macquer's "calcination of the first kind," which meant all experiments on limestone, hartshorn, the *coraux rouges,* and similar substances that had encumbered and confused the earlier reports. Even when confining his study to calcinable metals, Guyton believed it was important to ignore all cases where the metal appreciably volatilizes or sublimes; for this reason he performed no experiments with mercury or with certain of the demimetals, for example, arsenic.[58]

He was quite insistent about the experimental procedures to be followed, rejecting experiments performed with the burning glass as wholly unreliable—though some

[54] *Digressions académiques,* pp. 39–40.   [55] *Ibid.,* p. 61.
[56] *Ibid.,* pp. 41–45, 51–54.   [57] *Ibid.,* pp. 46–48.
[58] *Ibid.,* pp. 66–67.

of the most famous results had been obtained in this way —for in such experiments it is difficult to avoid spattering, fuming, and consequent loss of material. Indeed, Guyton believed that this might explain the extraordinary results reported by Hartsoeker, who kept lead—where the fact of augmentation was so well attested—for several days at the focus of a burning glass without noting any gain in weight. All metals should be calcined, Guyton advised, over an ordinary chemist's fire or in a furnace.[59]

But other experimental precautions must also be carefully observed. Earthenware vessels should be preheated to drive off any moisture and to ensure that they had been properly baked in the manufacture. It is of the utmost importance to carry all calcinations through to completion, for ambiguous results will be obtained if the experimenter uses too feeble a fire or too short an exposure.[60] During the heating the metal must be freely exposed to the air, for it is a well-known principle—which Guyton confirmed by a control experiment—that calcination (like combustion) cannot take place if air is excluded. Of particular importance, as Guyton learned from his own experience, was the precaution of stirring the melt at regular intervals to expose all parts of it to the air.

Guyton then gives the results of his carefully conducted experiments on the calcination of copper, iron filings, filings of fine English steel, tin, metallic antimony, bismuth, and zinc.[61] He did not trouble to confirm the well-known instance of lead. Weighed samples of each metal were heated in open crucibles or dishes over a fire or under the muffle of a cupellation furnace, using exposures

[59] *Ibid.*, pp. 65–66.   [60] *Ibid.*, pp. 63 and 65.
[61] *Ibid.*, pp. 72–87.

of from one to five hours. All the metals were weighed again after calcination and gave unequivocal evidence of an augmentation in weight. For each metal, when the calcination was brought to completion, he found a characteristic increase in weight. In his experiments with iron filings he followed the progress of the calcination under different conditions by testing the mass at various intervals with a magnet. In the case of the copper filings he showed how the magnitude of the effect varied when the copper was slowly heated and regularly stirred with a polished steel rod, when it was calcined without stirring, and when an attempt was made to calcine it in a covered and hermetically sealed vessel containing only a small amount of air.

The last experiment is worth describing, since the result was certainly such as to interest Lavoisier. Indeed, it may have been to confirm Guyton's result that Lavoisier suggested in the August memorandum an experiment to be carried out with the burning glass and closed vessels to see whether metals could be calcined in a limited amount of air. Guyton placed a half-ounce of copper shavings (*rognures de feuilles de cuivre*) in a small covered porcelain vessel. This he heated under a muffle for five hours over a fire strong enough to deform the vessel and seal the cover so tightly that it had to be broken to get at the contents. He found hardly any evidence of calcination and noted that the weight of the copper seemed to have decreased by about half a grain, and he concluded that his experiment had confirmed the widely accepted fact that calcination, like combustion, cannot readily occur in closed vessels.[62] Why this was the case, he did not try to explain.

[62] *Ibid.*, pp. 74–75.

The Reception of Guyton's Experiments

The historical and experimental parts of Guyton's memoir must command our genuine respect; they constitute a levelheaded, well-conducted piece of quantitative research on a timely problem. And there is little doubt that it settled the basic factual question which chemists were debating and made it as certain as such things can be that the common metals all gain weight when they are calcined.

The influence of Guyton's work was felt well before the appearance in print of the *Digressions académiques*. As early as the summer of 1771 he submitted his "Dissertation sur le phlogistique" to the Royal Academy of Sciences in Paris, hoping that it might prove acceptable for publication under the Academy's auspices in the next volume of the *Mémoires des savants étrangers*. Two senior chemists, P. J. Malouin (1701–1777) and the eminent P. J. Macquer, with whom Guyton had been in correspondence since early 1769, were chosen to read and referee the manuscript.

At a meeting of the Academy of Sciences—held on Saturday, February 8, 1772, in the accustomed rooms in the Louvre—Macquer read a long report on the "Mémoire de M. Demorveau sur le phlogistique," which he had prepared with Malouin. Lavoisier, the young *adjoint chimiste*, was in attendance and could scarcely have failed to be impressed by what he heard, for the greater part of the session was devoted to Macquer's highly laudatory report.[63]

Macquer described Guyton's essay as a "grand travail

[63] *Procès-verbaux*, 91 (1772), fols. 31 verso to 36 recto.

. . . sur un des objets des plus interessants at des plus élevés de la Chimie." Although the work as a whole was praised for the cogency and clarity of its reasoning, it was the "suite complete des plus belles expériences qui forment le fond de sa dissertation" which aroused special admiration. And the report continued:

On doit distinguer deux objets dans cet ouvrage, l'un sistematique, que nous avons exposé, l'autre expérimental, et tendant uniquement à établir le fait fondamental de l'augmentation du poids absolu des corps par la soustraction de leur principe inflammable; le premier nous parait susceptible de difficultés. . . . A l'égard de la partie expérimentale de l'ouvrage de M. de Morveau, elle nous parait mériter les plus grands éloges, et d'autant plus digne d'approbation de l'Académie qu'elle constate et generalize le plus grand nombre des moïens que peut fournir la chimie un fait très important, jusqu'à présent trop peu décidé et trop particulier.[64]

Here, in the considered judgment of two of the Academy's outstanding chemists, was immediate (and official) recognition that, while the explanation of the phenomenon studied by Guyton was not wholly satisfactory, his experiments had clearly established the reality and generality of a phenomenon about which the evidence had been fragmentary (*trop particulier*) and contradictory and chemical opinion "trop peu décidé."

Guyton's work was taken up again when the Academy met a week later to hear Macquer conclude his report on the essay. Despite its merits, and because of its length and the author's plan to include the "Dissertation" in a forth-

[64] *Ibid.*, fol. 35 verso.

coming book, the Academy declined to include it in the next *Savants étrangers*. This was fair enough; the *Digressions académiques* must have been nearly ready for the printer and perhaps only awaited the approval of the royal censor; for the *approbation*, signed by Macquer, is dated March 19, 1772, and the book was in fact published before the month of June.[65] But Guyton, though denied a double publication, had reason to be satisfied. It was at this meeting of February 15 that the gifted amateur chemist of Dijon, who had been rejected as a candidate six months before, was nominated once again for the post of corresponding member of the Paris Academy; this time he was successfully elected.[66]

Contemporary praise was not confined to the halls of the Louvre, and there is ample evidence that Guyton's "Digressions" was deemed a contribution of real significance. Its influence is immediately traceable in the published literature. In 1773 Baumé—who ten years earlier had expressed doubts about the reality of the augmentation effect—could write in his *Chymie expérimentale et*

[65] So Speter ("Lavoisierana," *loc. cit.*, p. 994). This seems correct, for Macquer presented a copy to the Academy of Sciences on Guyton's behalf at the meeting of June 3, 1772 (*Procès-verbaux*, 91 [1772], fol. 193 verso). Lavoisier noted this in his *plumitif*, or personal record of the meeting, remarking that Guyton's book "se vent chez Didot à Paris," a significant expression of his interest. On June 5 Buffon wrote Guyton from Montbard acknowledging a complimentary copy. See Jean Pelseneer, "Une lettre inédite de Buffon à Guyton de Morveau à propos du phlogistique," in Léon Bertin *et al.*, *Buffon* (Paris, 1952), pp. 133–136.

[66] *Ibid.*, fol. 47 verso. He was duly elected at the meeting of March 7, and made the correspondent of Macquer. Cf. *Index biographique des membres et correspondants de l'Académie des sciences, de 1666 à 1939* (Paris, 1939), p. 209.

raisonnée that each type of metal augments in a constant manner during calcination.[67] An anonymous review of the *Digressions académiques,* which appeared in the April, 1773, number of the *Journal encyclopédique,* had high praise for Guyton's experimental work.[68] And the Marquis de Condorcet, of whose interest in the calcination problem we shall shortly speak, fully appreciated the significance of Guyton's experiments. Writing in 1773 of the increase in the weight of metals on calcination as "un des phénomènes les plus extraordinaires que présente la chimie," Condorcet continued:

M. de Morveau, procureur général au parlement de Dijon, vient de faire sur cet objet des recherches très-étendues: il a prouvé que cette augmentation était réelle et générale pour tous les métaux, ce que quelques chimistes avaient nié. On trouve dans son ouvrage une suite intéressante d'expériences faites avec un soin et une sagacité peu communes, qui le

[67] Baumé, *Chymie expérimentale et raisonnée,* I, 59, and II, 265. Baumé was at work on his book in the summer of 1772, for he quotes the *Avant-coureur* for May 11 (I, 112, note). Yet in the "Avertissement" (I, p. xx) he writes with reference to his treatment of phlogiston that this "article étoit imprimé lorsque parut l'excellente Dissertation de M. Guitton [*sic*] de Morveau, Avocat Général du Parlement de Dijon; sans cette circonstance, j'aurois fait usage avec reconnoissance de plusieurs grandes vues que cet habile Physicien propose" (I, 145–161). This refers to the theoretical section of Guyton's work. Though not yet a member of the Academy, Baumé certainly knew, if only through Macquer, of the experimental results which Guyton had reported to the Academy in 1771.

[68] "Ce que les chymistes trouveront de meilleur & de plus essentiel dans cette partie de l'ouvrage de M. de Morveau, ce sont les faits & les expériences qu'il rapporte sur la réduction [*sic*] des métaux en chaux" (*Journal encyclopédique,* April, 1773, p. 87).

rendront toujours précieux, quand même l'auteur se serait
égaré dans la nouvelle explication qu'il propose pour ce
phénomène.[69]

The final accolade was accorded a few years later when
Macquer, the correspondent and early sponsor of Guyton,
wrote as follows on the subject of the calcination of metals
in the second and greatly revised edition of his *Dictionnaire de chymie* (1778):

Nous n'avons encore qu'un très petit nombre de Chymistes
modernes qui aient commencé à s'en occuper. Ils ont tourné
principalement leurs vues sur un phénomene frappant & qui
paroît appartenir aux chaux métalliques, de quelque maniere
que les métaux aient été réduits sous cette forme, je veux parler
de l'augmentation de poids très sensible qu'on remarque dans
la plupart de ces chaux; je dis la plupart, attendu qu'il n'est
pas encore bien constaté que cet effet ait lieu pour tous les
métaux; mais enfin, comme on l'a observé dans un grand nombre, ainsi que l'a très bien exposé un Savant, qui a vraiment le
génie de la Physique & de la Chymie, on peut supposer que
ce phénomene est général.[70]

In restrospect Guyton himself laid stress on this accomplishment. In 1786 he wrote that if Lavoisier had finally
demonstrated the cause of the increase in weight of
calcined metals by his "belle expérience" of heating tin

[69] *Oeuvres de Condorcet,* II, 38–39.

[70] P. J. Macquer, *Dictionnaire de chymie* (2nd ed.; Paris: Chez
P. Didot jeune, 1778), I, 346–347. The "savant" is identified in a
footnote as "M. de *Morveau,* Avocat Général au Parlement de
Dijon."

and lead in closed vessels, it was he, Guyton, who had first established the reality and the generality of the phenomenon which Lavoisier explained. After a description of Lavoisier's experiment, he wrote:

Les hypothèses proposées pour l'explication de ce phénomène présentoient tant de difficultés, qu'un grand nombre de Physiciens préféroit encore de laisser le fait en question; je crois avoir contribué à en établir la réalité par les expériences nombreuses que je publiai en 1772 (*Digressions académiques,* &c), expériences qui, par la conformité des résultats obtenus des divers procédés de calcination & par les proportions déterminées de cet accroissement de poids suivant la nature de chaque métal, ne permettoient plus de l'attribuer à quelqu'accident.[71]

It is my belief that Lavoisier's interest in the calcination problem was first aroused, not only by meditating about the effervescence of metallic calxes during reduction, but also by the discussions which Guyton's experiments evoked in 1771–1772 and by the evident incompatibility between the newly established *fait capital* and the phlogiston theory to which Guyton tenaciously adhered. Guyton's procrustean efforts to accommodate theory to experiment, I feel sure, caused Lavoisier to ponder the inherent contradiction and to search for a new explanation of the phenomenon itself.[72]

[71] *Encyclopédie méthodique—Chimie,* I (1786), 699.

[72] This interpretation was first set forth in a paper entitled "What Made Lavoisier Study Calcination," read at a meeting of the History of Science Society in New York on December 20, 1948. On this occasion I reported also on Turgot's surprising anticipation of

If this is so, and if Lavoisier was led in this manner to speculate on the causes of calcination, we might expect to find some testimony to this effect from Lavoisier himself, or at least some reference to the significance of Guyton's experiments.

Yet in print Lavoisier never acknowledged this debt, and indeed scarcely refers to Guyton's early work. There is no mention of Guyton or the *Digressions académiques* in the *Opuscules* (1774); and if the man who later became his disciple is several times cited by Lavoisier in his *Traité élémentaire de chimie*, it is chiefly for Guyton's theories of affinity and his contribution to the reform of chemical nomenclature. In the posthumous *Mémoires de chimie* (1805), where there is a short history of the calcination problem—and where, of all places, he might be expected to mention Guyton's discovery—Lavoisier merely speaks of Guyton's "efforts infructueux" to explain, by means of the phlogistic hypothesis, the increase in weight of calcined metals; there is no reference to Guyton's experiments.[73] The sole published evidence I can find for Guyton's influence on Lavoisier is in a paper that the latter read to the Academy in 1783 on the precipitation of metals from their solutions. Here, for three pages, Lavoisier makes use of Guyton's figures for the characteristic increase in weight of the different metals. The experiments are treated with respect, and Guyton is

Lavoisier's discovery. A brief statement of my views concerning Guyton's influence on Lavoisier is given in my recent paper, "Some French Antecedents of the Chemical Revolution," *loc. cit.*, p. 110.

[73] *Mémoires de chimie*, II, 78; reprinted in *Oeuvres de Lavoisier*, II, 99–104. Nor is there any reference to Guyton's experiments in Lavoisier's "Rapport à l'Académie sur les travaux de Guyton de Morveau," in *Oeuvres*, VI, 56–58.

praised for having obtained satisfactory results in the difficult case of zinc.[74]

This is all, and it is not much, from the record printed in Lavoisier's lifetime. Privately, he was more generous. On January 19, 1774, Lavoisier sent Guyton a complimentary copy of his recently published *Opuscules,* as he did to those others—like the various surviving pioneers in pneumatic chemistry—whose work he had found useful. This would seem to testify to the respect in which Lavoisier held Guyton's book; and, in fact, Lavoisier said as much in the covering letter. After remarking that he would soon be obliged to refute Guyton's theory of the role of phlogiston, he wrote:

Mais en osant attaquer votre oppinion, je declarerai toujours que vos digressions accademiques portent partout lempreinte du genie dobservation, et quon y trouve la Suitte dexperiences la plus Complette la plus interessante la plus exacte qui existe Sur la Calcination des metaux.[75]

It would be hard to state the case more strongly, or in fact more justly; it is regrettable that Lavoisier never said as much in print. That he was not indulging in mere flattery is confirmed by a hitherto unpublished note, which I was fortunate to discover among the Lavoisier papers in the archives of the Academy of Sciences in Paris. It is undated, very short, and worth reproducing in full:

Sur la matiere du feu

Tous les metaux exposes au feu et calcines augmentent de poids tres sensiblement.

[74] "Mémoire sur la précipitation des substances métalliques les unes par les autres," *Oeuvres de Lavoisier,* II, 528–545.

[75] *Oeuvres de Lavoisier—Correspondance,* II, 404–406.

Les auteurs anciens pretendoient qu'on combinoit du feu avec ces corps dans la calcination et que c'etoit à l'addition de cette Substance pesante qu'on devoit l'augmentation du poids.

Sthal [*sic*] a pretendu que la calcination enlevoit la matiere du feu aux corps qu'on calcinoit mais lui et ses sectateurs sont tombes dans un labirinte de difficultes comment concevoir en effet qu'on augmente le poids d'un corps en lui enlevant une partie de sa substance.

Quoi qu'il en soit de l'explication, le fait n'en est pas moins constant. Tous les metaux augmentent de poids par la calcination. M. de Morvaux [*sic*] le demontre complettement dans Ses digressions academiques page 72 jusqu'à 88.[76]

It is likely that this revealing note was written in the summer or early autumn of 1772, after the publication of the *Digressions académiques* (which had appeared by early June) but before Lavoisier had carried out those experiments in October which convinced him of the real explanation of the phenomenon. I should guess it to have been written at roughly the same time as the August memorandum.

Guyton's experiments, then, served to convince Lavoisier that the augmentation of the calx was a general effect observed with all calcinable metals, but we know that Lavoisier found utterly preposterous Guyton's attempt to explain the effect in terms of the phlogiston theory. Sometime in the summer of 1772, before he wrote the August memorandum, several factors which we have

[76] Lavoisier papers, archives of the Academy of Sciences, Paris, dossier 14. This two-page note seems to have been written on paper of the sort Lavoisier used for scattered notes during the period 1772–1773.

suggested—the effervescence of calxes during reduction, the fact (which Guyton had supported) that metals resist calcination in closed vessels, the first inklings of work on gases being carried out abroad,[77] and Hales's familiar doctrine of fixed air—combined to suggest to Lavoisier a more likely explanation: that the air fixed in metals during calcination and released upon reduction might account for the greater weight of a calx.[78]

[77] That in Sweden Torbern Bergman, too, was already working on "fixed air" was known to Lavoisier. Macquer wrote to Bergman on July 18, 1772, that he had announced to the Academy "votre travail sur ce qu'on appelle (sans doute fort improprement) *air fixe*. elle ne doute pas, d'après l'idée avantageuse qu'elle a conçue de vos talens, par la lecture [in April, 1772] de votre mémoire sur l'or fulminant, que vous ne poussiez très loin cette découverte, et elle en attend le resultat avec empressement." This letter is to appear in Johan Nordström, *The Foreign Correspondence of Torbern Bergman*, in press. Photocopies of proof sheets were kindly put at my disposal by my friend Dr. Uno Boklund.

[78] Hales might, indeed, have supplied Lavoisier's clue. J. Martin Clare wrote: "The Change of Weight of Bodies in chemical Preparations heretofore presumed to rise from the Adhesion of Particles of Fire, is proved by Dr. Hales, in his *Vegetable Staticks*, to proceed from the Adhesion of Particles of Air, which he has there shewed to be absorb'd by some Bodies in good Quantities, while it has been generated as fast by others" (*Motion of Fluids* [3rd ed.; London, 1747], p. 300).

CHAPTER 5

A Striking Anticipation of
Lavoisier's Theory

THAT Lavoisier's epoch-making experiments of the autumn of 1772 were in large measure a consequence of the convergent influences upon him of Stephen Hales and Guyton de Morveau seems highly probable from the evidence already set forth. This conclusion gains strong, if indirect, support from the remarkable fact that another contemporary Frenchman independently set down an identical conclusion, nearly a year before Lavoisier, about the role of air in calcination; and though he may have hit upon the idea even earlier, he was stimulated to formulate it fully and clearly by the same influences. A striking anticipation of Lavoisier's hypothesis—an anticipation which, though he did not confirm it by experiment, is closer to Lavoisier's idea than the much-cited speculations of Jean Rey and Père Béraut [1]—must be

[1] As already pointed out, Rey believed that particles of air, rendered adhesive by heat, combined with the calx but did not produce it; and Béraut, like Du Clos, thought that impurities in the air were responsible. See the detailed summary of Béraut's views by McKie, "Béraut's Theory of Calcination," *loc. cit.*, pp. 284–289.

credited to an unexpected person: Anne Robert Jacques
Turgot (1721–1781), the distinguished *philosophe*, economist, and French public servant. A man of wide-ranging
interests, an enthusiastic amateur of science who had
studied chemistry under Lavoisier's teacher, G. F. Rouelle,
Turgot in 1771 was *intendant,* or chief officer of the
Crown, for the generality of Limoges.[2] Despite the pressure of his duties he found time to carry on a chatty,
philosophical correspondence, touching on all manner of
timely questions, with the young Marquis de Condorcet,
the gifted mathematician of the Academy of Sciences.
The correspondence is particularly full and interesting
for the years that especially concern us here, i.e., 1771–
1773.[3] Condorcet seems to have taken it upon himself
to keep Turgot abreast of doings in the capital; and
although many of his letters are filled with personal and
literary gossip, there are a number devoted to scientific

[2] Turgot's scientific interests are treated lightly by his biographers. For the scientific side of his association with his friend
Madame d'Enville (1716–1794) and her son, the Duc de la
Rochefoucauld d'Enville (1743–1792), there is some information
in Emile Rousse, *La Roche-Guyon, châtelains, château et bourg*
(Paris, 1892). Turgot's most significant scientific publication is his
long and interesting article "Expansibilité" in the *Encyclopédie*
(VI [1756], 274–285). See his extensive corrections and additions
in the errata (VII [1757], 1028–1029). In 1775 Lavoisier referred
to this article as "rempli des vues les plus vastes & les plus neuves,
& qui porte par-tout l'empreinte du génie" (*Observations sur la
physique,* 5 [1775], 429). This was probably a gesture of ingratia-
tion rather than a scientific judgment on Lavoisier's part, for when
he wrote in the spring of 1775 Turgot was Controller-General of
Finance and had just organized the Régie des poudres to which he
appointed Lavoisier in June.
[3] Henry, *Correspondance inédite de Condorcet et de Turgot,*
pp. 33–156.

topics. The first reference to our subject is in a letter of Condorcet dated August 2, 1771:

Nous avons à l'Académie un excellent mémoire de chimie qui nous vient d'un conseiller au Parlement de Dijon. Il a pour objet l'augmentation du poids réel des métaux par la calcination. Il a fait sur ce sujet beaucoup de nouvelles expériences, et il prétend que le Phlogistique n'est pas attiré par chaque molécule de matière terrestre comme les autres corps et qu'au contraire il est animé de forces qui lui donnent une direction contraire à celle de la pesanteur.[4]

Fortunately, Turgot's long and detailed reply—dated Limoges, August 16, 1771—has been preserved. It is an extraordinarily interesting letter, which, if echoes of it ever came to Lavoisier's ears, would surely earn Turgot something more than a footnote in a history of the Chemical Revolution. To be appreciated it should be read in its entirety; I shall only summarize it with a few key excerpts.

Turgot finds Guyton's explanation of the augmentation effect—as somewhat misrepresented by Condorcet, who had not yet read the work—to be wholly absurd, and he writes:

Je ne conçois pas comment les chimistes n'ont pas encore pensé à expliquer le phénomène en question par une cause qui se présente d'elle-même et que j'aurais publiée il y a bien long temps si j'avais le loisir de faire des expériences. Cependant je la crois prouvée par un assez grand nombre d'inductions pour etre très-persuadé que c'est la vraie.

[4] *Ibid.*, p. 58.

After arguing that something must be added to the metal
if its weight is increased and after dismissing the possibility that light might be responsible, he continues:

> Puisque la lumière ne peut augmenter le poids du métal
> calciné, il faut donc voir s'il n'y a pas dans le voisinage du
> métal quelqu'autre matière qui puisse s'y unir pendant le cours
> de l'opération.

This substance can only be air, which possesses weight, is
abundantly available, and is known to combine with other
principles of bodies to produce many different compounds
(*mixtes*):

> Il est certain par une foule d'expériences, et en particulier
> par celles de Stales [*sic*], que cet air combiné entre dans la
> composition des corps les plus durs et contribue à leur liaison
> et à leur dureté, ainsi que l'eau fait la liaison et la dureté des
> marbres, ainsi que le phlogistique fait la liaison des métaux.

Air combines or is given off in different chemical operations depending upon whether its affinity for the substance with which it is combined is greater or smaller
than for other substances to which it is exposed. Effervescences encountered in familiar chemical reactions are produced by bubbles of air released from combination. Since
air can combine with bodies

> et puisqu'il n'y a que de l'air à la portée du métal qui se
> calcine, il faut bien en conclure que l'augmentation de poids
> survenue à ce métal est due à l'air qui, dans l'opération de
> la combustion, s'est uni à la terre métallique et a pris la place

du Phlogistique qui s'est brûlé et qui sans être léger d'une légèreté absolue est incomparablement moins pesant que l'air, apparemment parce qu'il contient moins de matière.[5]

It is really surprising that this letter, with its remarkable anticipation of Lavoisier's own explanation and its reference to "Stales" (which should evidently be read as "Hales," not, as a later editor believed, as "Stahl"), should have escaped notice.[6] Here, with much greater precision and clarity than Jean Rey, Du Clos, or Père Béraut—none of whom, in any event, he had reason to have read— Turgot suggests that calcined metals increase in weight by a combination with air. That Turgot, unlike Rey and

[5] *Ibid.*, pp. 59–62. This letter, with others of Turgot to Condorcet from this correspondence, can also be found in Gustave Schelle, *Oeuvres de Turgot et documents le concernant* (Paris, 1913–1923), III, 542–547.

[6] In reproducing this passage from Charles Henry's version, Schelle changed the reading from "Stales" to "Stahl." Perhaps Turgot had written "S. Hales," for it makes little sense to attribute to Stahl (who firmly denied the chemical role of air) experiments on the combination of air with bodies. But perhaps Turgot was originally at fault; elsewhere he writes: "Ces messieurs [Venel and Macquer] avaient rappelé à une meilleure théorie et ils avaient étendu les conséquences des premières expériences de Stahl, lequel est vraiment le premier qui ait aperçu le rôle que l'air joue dans la nature comme principe des mixtes; mais toutes les idées spéculatives de Stahl, toutes les conséquences qu'il tire des faits qu'il a vus sont infiniment embrouillés et manquent de cette dialectique, de cette précision d'idées et de langage dont jusqu'ici les physiciens se sont occupés beaucoup trop peu" (letter of November 27, 1772, *ibid.*, p. 111). This reference to the style of Stahl suggests a genuine confusion. Rhoda Rappaport believes that Turgot, as a pupil of Rouelle, is reflecting the Stahlianism of his teacher, which, as she has pointed out, was combined with the teachings of Hales. The two names were sometimes confused by Rouelle's auditors.

Béraut, was thinking of a definite chemical reaction, is evident from the following sentence:

> Le magasin qui fournit à cette augmentation ne manquera pas puisque l'atmosphère fournit toujours de l'air à mesure que la terre métallique en absorbe. Cette absorption a ses limites ou son point de saturation comme toute les unions chimiques et c'est cette saturation qui établit le rapport de l'augmentation du poids dans les differents métaux calcinés.[7]

Then, soon after, comes the most striking passage in this truly remarkable letter:

> Au surplus, cette calcination des métaux devrait être appelée combustion; ce n'est qu'une branche du grand phénomène de la combustion par lequel le phlogistique uni aux principes terreux s'en dégage à un degré de chaleur constant dans chaque corps, mais vraisemblablement variable dans les différents corps à raison de la force de l'union. . . .
> Il suit de là que le phénomène de l'augmentation du poids devrait être général dans la combustion de tous les corps; je voudrais constater cette conséquence par des expériences. . . . Mais le temps me manque et j'avoue que sans nouvelles expériences les inductions tirées de celles qui sont déjà faites me paraissent donner à cette théorie une probabilité fort approchante de la certitude.[8]

Condorcet commented favorably on Turgot's theory in a letter of September 10, 1771, expressing approval of his

[7] *Correspondence inédite*, p. 62.
[8] *Ibid.*, pp. 62–63. As an experimental test of his theory, Turgot suggests treating calxes (*cendres métalliques*) with acids, to see if more air is driven off than when the pure metal is similarly dissolved. The result would certainly have confused him, but he did not perform the experiments.

correspondent's suggestion and remarking that "il faudrait qu'un chimiste suivît votre explication et imaginât des expériences décisives pour ou contre. C'est une des questions les plus importantes qu'on puisse agiter dans cette science." [9] But it was not until July, 1772, that Condorcet wrote that he had finally read Guyton's essay, almost certainly as printed in the *Digressions* [10] which had just appeared a month earlier. Though the subject is discussed in later letters exchanged between Turgot and Condorcet in the autumn of 1772, we need not follow the correspondence further, for by now Lavoisier had moved to the center of the stage and was hard at work, determinedly, albeit quietly.

One question forces itself upon us: did Condorcet, not always the most discreet or reticent of men, disclose to his colleague, Lavoisier, the theory that Turgot had advanced in the letter of August 16, 1771? It is impossible to tell, but I rather think—from a remark in a letter of Condorcet to Turgot—that he did not. On December 5, 1772, Condorcet asked Turgot whether he should mention the latter's conjectures in a eulogy of the chemist Du Clos which he was preparing, especially if Turgot did not expect to perform the necessary experiments in the near future.[11]

[9] *Ibid.*, pp. 69–71.

[10] *Ibid.*, pp. 93–95. "J'ai lu l'ouvrage de M. de Morvaux [*sic*] sur le phlogistique, je n'en suis pas mécontent; mais il est au-dessous de ce que j'en espérais." The fact that he also writes that he has read Guyton "sur la dissolution et les cristallisations" makes it clear that Condorcet had been reading the printed *Digressions,* which includes an essay on this subject.

[11] *Ibid.*, pp. 117–118. Condorcet is here referring to his *Histoire de l'Académie ou des académiciens morts avant 1699,* published early in 1773 and reviewed in the April 15 issue of the *Journal encyclopédique,* pp. 248–259. Condorcet undertook this project

This seems to imply that Condorcet had been discreetly silent about his friend's disclosure, though he may have made a distinction between publishing Turgot's theory and confiding it, or hinting at it, by word of mouth. Yet Condorcet could hardly have kept the matter wholly to himself, for we find him writing to Turgot, late in November, that he and a chemist of the Academy, B. G. Sage, were about to collaborate on an experiment, which we have described above, to see if fixed air is produced when a metallic calx is reduced.[12] Condorcet could hardly have failed to discuss with Sage the significance of this experiment in the light of Turgot's conjecture, if indeed it was not Turgot's letter that suggested it; but there is no evidence that he mentioned the matter to Lavoisier. It is evident, at least, that Lavoisier, who had deposited

to advance his ambitions to succeed Grandjean de Fouchy, the aged and ineffectual Perpetual Secretary of the Academy of Sciences. In April, 1773, Condorcet won out in a bitterly contested election over the astronomer, Jean-Sylvain Bailly, the candidate backed by Buffon, and was named "secrétaire perpétuel en survivance." For an account of this event see Jean Nourrisson, *Trois révolutionnaires, Turgot, Necker, Bailly* (Paris, 1885), pp. 46 and 338–340.

[12] *Correspondance inédite*, p. 108. For the projected experiment of Sage and Condorcet see above, pp. 109–110. On November 22, 1772, Turgot wrote disparagingly (*ibid.*, pp. 111–112) of the French having adopted "des Ecossais cette fausse et impropre dénomination d'air fixe," and expressed irritation that the "Ecossais" claimed to have discovered "ce que nous savions il y a plus de vingt ans." This reference to the "Ecossais" makes it evident that Turgot had by this time seen the recent issues of Rozier's journal. But in a note he speaks of having read the review of Priestley's *Directions* which had just appeared in the September *Monthly Review* (47 [1772], 227–230). Here we find a summary of the achievements of Hales, Brownrigg, MacBride, Cavendish, and Lane, but no mention of Black.

the famous sealed note only a month before, had not disclosed to Condorcet or Sage the secret of his first epoch-making experiments on combustion.

By resurrecting Turgot's unpublished conjectures and calling attention to his anticipation by a full year of Lavoisier's theory of the chemical role of air in calcination, I certainly do not wish to diminish the credit or tarnish the laurels the great French chemist has richly earned as one of the chief founders of modern chemistry. And I am reluctant to believe that Lavoisier was set on the path of his reform of chemistry by an indiscreet revelation on the part of Condorcet. There are instances enough in Lavoisier's career which have led scholars to question his generosity and that "delicatesse en Litterature et en Physique" he once spoke of, in a letter to Rozier, as essential in science.[13] We can dispense with another.

Despite some resemblances in the details of their theories,[14] I prefer to think we are confronted with an extraordinarily clear-cut example of parallel thinking where two contemporaries, exposed to the same influences and meditating on the same phenomenon, came to an identical conclusion. Both men were familiar with Hales's doctrine of fixed air, though they knew little or nothing of the more recent work done in Britain; both interpreted effer-

[13] *Oeuvres de Lavoisier—Correspondance*, II, 465.

[14] There is a vague similarity between the theory Lavoisier sets forth in his "Système sur les élémens" and the remark in Turgot's letter of August 16, 1771, where air, water, and phlogiston are compared as binding agents when fixed in bodies. One could perhaps point to Turgot's suggestion (cf. note 8 above) that calxes might be treated with acid to see if more air is given off than by the corresponding pure metal. This problem was later raised by Lavoisier in the August memorandum.

vescences as the release of combined air; and to each of them an application of these facts came to mind when they speculated on calcination and reduction and learned of Guyton's experiments on the increased weight of calcined metals. To both men—alike anxious to see chemistry develop in the quantitative spirit of "la saine physique"— the combination of air with a metal was a more likely explanation of the augmentation effect than those fancies of Guyton which violated the accepted principles of Newtonian physics. What Turgot's letter does for us is to make explicit the principal influences we rather laboriously deduced as having shaped Lavoisier's thought and determined its direction.

CHAPTER 6

Lavoisier, Phosphorus, and the Role of Mitouard

THERE still remains an unexplained aspect of the early combustion experiments of Lavoisier. As we have seen, he had planned—as early as August 8, 1772—to investigate the calcination and reduction of metals in closed vessels using the burning glass and a modification of Hales's pedestal apparatus. Yet it is well known, and we have repeatedly emphasized, that the first experiments he actually performed were those on phosphorus and sulphur and that the famous reduction of minium was not carried out until late October. If possible, we should account for this delay and ask ourselves in what manner— after having hit upon the idea that air might combine with metals—he was led to investigate the possible absorption of air by burning phosphorus.

The Minium Experiment

To understand the delay we must say a word or two more about Lavoisier's activities during the summer and early fall of 1772. In the spring of that year—when with Macquer and Cadet he was experimenting on the diamond—it was several times remarked that the conflicting results obtained by different workers might be due to a failure to employ sufficiently high, and therefore, for all practical purposes, sufficiently comparable, furnace temperatures. It was proposed that the experiments be repeated by the spectacular method of the earlier Florentine experimenters, namely, by employing a powerful burning mirror or burning glass. This, it was pointed out, would ensure temperatures immeasurably higher than any that could be supplied by a furnace. After some preliminary tests Cadet and Brisson asked the Academy, in July, for permission to take from its cabinet of curiosities the great lens of Tschirnhausen which had been used earlier in the century by Homberg and Geoffroy for their experiments on various mineral substances and in the focus of which Homberg, for example, claimed he had calcined and vitrified gold.[1]

The Academy readily granted this request and at the same time extended an invitation to other members—in particular, Macquer and Lavoisier—to share in the pro-

[1] See Macquer's report on these experiments (*Introduction aux observations*, II, 612–616). A more detailed account of the preparations is given by Lavoisier in an unpublished manuscript; he attributes the initiative to Cadet, who believed the use of a burning glass would provide evidence for or against his decrepitation theory and who performed with Brisson some preliminary experiments with a small burning glass belonging to the latter. Finding this too small to be effective, he thought of asking the Academy for the use of the Tschirnhausen lens, the so-called "lentille du Palais Royal," and in July "MM. Cadet et Brisson demanderent a l'academie la permission de tirer de Son Cabinet et la lentille et Sa monture aussy que quelques autres instrumens qui paroissoient necessaires pour Cette Operation" (Lavoisier papers, archives of the Academy of Sciences, dossier 72 J, see Appendix II).

posed experiments. The investigators needed a location in the open air, where they could erect a shed or conservatory (*un hangard ou espèce de serre*) to house and shelter the lens. The site hit upon was the so-called "Jardin de l'Infante," a terrace running southward from the old Louvre to the quai and adjacent to a ground-floor apartment of the palace, which could be at the disposal of the experimenters. By a further piece of good fortune a second Tschirnhausen lens, with the same diameter as the Academy's lens but with a shorter focal length, was lent by its owner, the Comte de la Tour d'Auvergne. The investigators were thus able to begin their experiments by the middle of August, 1772, with the two largest and strongest lenses yet made.

Lavoisier was actively engaged in this collaborative investigation from August 14, when the first experiment was carried out, until October 13. He had definite ideas as to how the equipment might profitably be used; indeed, as I have argued, the document he drew up on August 8, entitled "Réflexions sur les expériences qu'on peut tenter à l'aide du miroir ardent," was neither a memoir intended for publication, as some have claimed, nor yet a purely private memorandum, but a set of proposals intended to influence his coworkers.[2] In this August memorandum Lavoisier suggested some experiments on minerals, stones, and refractory materials; but, as we have seen, he was particularly interested in work on the diamond and still more so in possible experiments on heating metals and metallic calxes in closed vessels.

The detailed record of these experiments makes it clear that Lavoisier's most striking proposals were for the most

[2] See my "Lost Memoir of Lavoisier," *loc. cit.*, p. 126.

part ignored, and that it was the interests of the others which determined the choice of the experiments actually performed. These consisted almost exclusively in subjecting a wide variety of metals and mineral substances to the action of the burning glass in the open air.[3] It is hardly surprising that Lavoisier was obliged thus to defer to his colleagues' wishes, and that his proposals were largely disregarded, for he was, after all, a junior of the group both in age and in academic rank.

It was not until the collaborative investigation was suspended in mid-October that Lavoisier was free to use the equipment for his own purposes. His historic experiments on minium were at last performed in the Jardin de l'Infante in the period between October 22 and November 1, using a simple adaptation of Hales's pedestal apparatus (Fig. 4).[4] In the center of a basin of water

[3] "Détails des expériences executées au moyen du grand verre ardent," *Oeuvres de Lavoisier*, III, 284–342. Lavoisier records: "MM. Cadet et Brisson Sentirent Combien il etoit importans de profitter de cette circonstance pour repeter tout ce qui avoit été fait par MM. homberg et Geoffroy avec le verre ardent et pour y ajouter de nouvelles experiences" (Lavoisier papers, dossier 72 J, fol. 1 verso).

[4] A full description is given in Chapter V of the second part of the *Opuscules* where Lavoisier writes: "J'ai mis dans la capsule A [Fig. 4] 2 gros de minium, mêlés avec 12 grains de braise de boulanger, qui avait été préalablement réduite en poudre et calcinée à un grand feu pendant plusieurs heures dans un vaisseau fermé; j'ai marqué, avec une bande de papier collé, la hauteur GH, jusqu'à laquelle j'avais élevé l'eau, et j'ai porté l'appareil, ainsi disposé, au foyer du grand verre ardent de Tschirnhausen, appartenant à M. le comte de la Tour d'Auvergne; cette lentille était alors établie au Louvre, dans le jardin de l'Infante, pour d'autres expériences faites en société par MM. Macquer, Brisson, Cadet et par moi, et dont une partie est déjà connue de l'Académie des sciences"

Lavoisier put a supporting column of crystal fixed in place by a bit of sealing wax; on top of it he placed a porcelain crucible. A crystal bell jar was inverted over the column with its crucible, and the basin was filled with water; when air was sucked out of the bell jar with a siphon, the water could be made to rise to any desired level, which Lavoisier then marked by a band of adhesive paper. A drop of oil was added on the surface of the water to prevent the discharged gas from dissolving. In the crucible he put his mixture of minium [5] and special charcoal (*braise de boulanger*) and brought it into the focus of the burning glass. The lead oxide was rapidly reduced, and from the fall of the water level Lavoisier was able to estimate the quantity of elastic fluid that was given off.

(*Oeuvres de Lavoisier*, I, 599–600). The apparatus, his modification of Hales's pedestal apparatus, is described on the same page.

[5] In the sealed note of November 1, where Lavoisier first refers to this experiment, he describes it as having been performed on "litharge"; here he refers to minium, which seems to be correct. Litharge, the reddish-yellow form of the monoxide (PbO), produced by fusing lead in open vessels, is described by Macquer (*Dictionnaire* [1766], II, 266) as "une substance jaunâtre vitrifiée, mais qui reste en especes de petites écailles comme talqueuses." Minium or red lead (Pb_3O_4), the scarlet crystalline powder resulting from further oxidation, was not readily produced in the laboratory in Lavoisier's time but was commercially available. Macquer says (*ibid.*, p. 123) that all the commercial minium was produced "en grand" in Dutch factories; he is not sure just how. Lavoisier, in his *registres* of 1773, is more careful about his terminology than he was in his sealed note; he cites numerous repetitions of his first experiment and refers in each case to the reduction of minium (Berthelot, *op. cit.*, pp. 237, 245, 248). Only in one place (*ibid.*, p. 238) does he refer to litharge, but this seems to refer back to an earlier experiment on the calcination of lead in which litharge was in fact produced, and not minium (*ibid.*, pp. 236–237).

With this apparatus Lavoisier repeated the experiment several times, using varying amounts of minium and charcoal before he hit upon the most effective proportions. Several bell jars were broken by the intense heat; and although he was unhappy at the small amounts of lead and charcoal he was obliged to use (because of the restricted focus of the burning glass), and at the necessity of using bell jars of large diameter (because of the intense heat in the neighborhood of the focus), he nevertheless found his result sufficiently decisive. The significance of this experiment was now far greater than when he had conceived it the previous summer; in the meantime, as we know, he had discovered that burning phosphorus and sulphur absorb large quantities of air, and he was now convinced that the addition of air accounted for the increase in weight of all substances that are burned or calcined.

The Combustion of Phosphorus and Sulphur

What then brought Lavoisier, during the period between August and late October, 1772, when he was obliged to postpone his experiment on the reduction of the calx of lead, to investigate the behavior of burning phosphorus and sulphur? There is no evidence, as we have seen, that either of these substances had interested him at any time before the autumn of 1772; he had never experimented with them, although the properties of phosphorus, in particular, had aroused the curiosity of a number of chemists.

This remarkable waxlike substance of extraordinary inflammability, with its striking property of shining in the dark, was still something of a novelty, though it had been known for more than a century. It was first discovered about 1668–1669 by an otherwise unknown Hamburg physician and chemist named Hennig Brand.[6] Brand's secret was earnestly sought by the more reputable chemist, Johann Kunckel, who journeyed to Hamburg only to find that a Dresden friend, a certain Johann Daniel Krafft (or Kraft), had forestalled him and purchased the secret for 200 thalers. Krafft made a good thing out of demonstrating the new substance, traveling to England, where he displayed it at the Court of Charles II and to gatherings of curious scientists. It was thus that Robert Boyle, in September, 1677, first learned of it. Like Kunckel, Boyle was fascinated, but he could extract from Krafft only the information that the new substance was prepared in some way from animal or human material. Both Kunckel and Boyle, independently and by their own exertions, discovered that phosphorus could be made by distilling evaporated urine. Kunckel disclosed his method to a number of persons; but in a work published in 1678, devoted to describing phosphorus and its properties, he neglected to tell precisely how he made it. Boyle in 1680–1682 was the first to publish a general method of preparing phosphorus and the first to give a really scientific account of some of its chemical and physical characteristics.[7]

[6] A good summary of the discovery and early history of phosphorus is given in Mary Elvira Weeks, *Discovery of the Elements* (6th ed.; Easton, Pa., 1956), pp. 122–139, with a valuable bibliography. But Kopp (*op. cit.*, III, 327–334) and Hoefer (*op. cit.*, II, 174–175 and 191–198) are still worth consulting.

[7] *Works of the Honourable Robert Boyle*, IV, 379–404 and 469–495. Boyle's chief assistant in this work, Ambrose Godfrey Hanckwitz (1660–1741), became Europe's chief supplier of phosphorus. See Hellot in *Mém. Acad. roy. sci.* for 1737 (1740), pp.

Boyle discovered that when phosphorus is ignited the product rapidly takes up moisture from the air to produce "a liquor almost as strong as spirit of salt," i.e., phosphoric acid. The acid was first carefully studied by the great German chemist, A. S. Marggraf (1709–1782), who prepared it from microcosmic salt, by burning phosphorus, and by treating phosphorus with nitric acid.[8] He carefully described the flocculent combustion product (P_4O_{10}) and called it flowers of phosphorus, because of its physical resemblance to flowers of zinc and similar substances. He made the important observation that this strongly hygroscopic material, if weighed while still warm (i.e., before it could take up water from the air) proved to be markedly heavier than the phosphorus from which it was made. But Marggraf made no attempt to explain this interesting phenomenon, and his observation did not attract wide notice.[9]

During the eighteenth century phosphorus—which the French chemists usually called Kunckel's phosphorus or English phosphorus to distinguish it from other phosphorescent substances—was prepared by the laborious and unpleasant method of Kunckel and Boyle, as improved by Hellot and later by Marggraf. In 1771 Scheele described a better method, evidently discovered accidentally by his colleague Gahn. This new process, in which phosphorus was prepared from bones, soon replaced the

---

342–378; and R. E. W. Maddison in *Notes and Records of the Royal Society of London*, 2 (1954–1955), 168–173.

[8] See Hoefer, *op. cit.*, II, 412, and Max Speter's article "Marggraf" in Bugge, *Das Buch der grossen Chemiker*, I, 228–239.

[9] This discovery was actually reported earlier by Godfrey Hanckwitz in *Philosophical Transactions*, 38 (1733–1734 [1735]), 58.

more repulsive older one. It is possible, but not likely, that the "beau phosphore venant d'Allemagne," which Lavoisier obtained for his use in September, 1772, was made according to Scheele's method. At this time Marggraf's procedure was the one commonly used.

Among Lavoisier's contemporaries there was much curiosity about phosphorus and its properties. Even the general public could learn something about this astonishing substance, for the conjuror Comus—a man of some scientific pretensions and immense popularity—used it with spectacular success in his mystifications.[10] Macquer included an exceedingly long article on phosphorus in his *Dictionnaire de chymie* of 1766, with a history of the substance and a full account of Marggraf's experiments. From him we learn that his disciple, Baumé the apothecary, was skilled in preparing phosphorus by an improved version of Marggraf's process.[11]

One French chemist we know to have been working with phosphorus is especially deserving of mention, since Meldrum has suggested his possible influence on Lavoisier, a conjecture that has often been repeated. This was B. G. Sage, a chemist and mineralogist already mentioned for his proposed experiment on the reduction of lead exide. In 1769, in his *Examen chymique de différentes substances minérales,* Sage reported that such concretions as the famous bezoar stone and other sorts of calculi contained salts of phosphoric acid.[12] Later he devoted

[10] For this man, whose real name was Nicolas Philippe Ledru, see Jean Torlais, "Un prestidigitateur célèbre," *Histoire de la médecine,* 5 (1955), 13–25.

[11] *Dictionnaire de chymie* (ed. 1766), II, 222–237.

[12] *Examen chymique de différentes substances minerales; essais sur le vin, les pierres, les bézoards, & d'autres parties d'histoire*

much space to discussing phosphorus and its acid in his *Elémens de minéralogie docimastique,* published early in 1772, but much of what he said in this book was highly fanciful and unsupported by a single experiment. He described phosphoric acid as "l'acide marin altéré par la circulation dans les corps des animaux carnivores" and therefore classed it with the mineral acids.[13] Sage accordingly tried to demonstrate the wide occurrence of phosphoric acid in the mineral kingdom, but rather unconvincingly, since he did not detect it in those minerals where it does in fact occur but believed that such diverse substances as borax, chalk, basalt, and the diamond were compounds of phosphoric acid.[14]

Meldrum, as we have seen, laid stress on the paper of Cigna that appeared in the May issue of Rozier's journal, which he thought could have influenced Lavoisier, since it "brought together numerous observations on the absorption of air" by burning phosphorus. This might be true, were it not for three things: (1) that Cigna in fact adds little to the observations of Stephen Hales, by whom he was strongly influenced and whom he frequently quotes; (2) that neither Hales nor Cigna clearly understood that air is chemically absorbed when phosphorus burns; and finally (3) that Lavoisier probably did not know the contents of Cigna's paper until many months later.

To take up the last objection first, there is persuasive evidence, which Meldrum overlooked, to show that La-

---

naturelle & de chymie; traduction d'une lettre de Monsieur Lehmann, sur la mine de plomb rouge (Paris, 1769), pp. 85–103.

[13] *Elémens de minéralogie docimastique* (ed. 1772), pp. 4–5.

[14] *Ibid.,* pp. 22, 38, 111, 132–133.

voisier had not read Cigna's memoir; or that, if he had, it made little or no impression upon him. For example, Lavoisier did not mention Cigna's work in the historical portion of the *Opuscules,* where he was at pains to bestow credit and to summarize all the important early work on "fixed air" and gases from Hales to Priestley, even including a short account of the work of Cigna's colleague, the Comte de Saluces, on the air released by the explosion of gunpowder. By the same token, Lavoisier did not send Cigna a complimentary copy of his book as he did, early in 1774, to Black, Priestley, De Smeth, Jacquin, and other pioneer pneumatic chemists. Nevertheless, he dispatched a copy, without specifying the recipient, to the Société Royale de Turin. The gift was acknowledged by a letter from the Comte de Saluces, who noted the omission of all reference to his colleague and urged Lavoisier to look up Cigna's paper in the second of the three volumes of the Turin *Mélanges* he was sending Lavoisier in return. Later that year Lavoisier received a letter from another Italian scientist, Father Beccaria, in which the latter spoke of experiments of his own and pointed out that they were briefly mentioned in the paper Cigna had published in the *Mélanges* of the Turin scientific society. The passage to which Beccaria referred had indeed appeared in Rozier's French version of the Cigna paper; but Lavoisier was evidently unaware of it, for he wrote to Rozier in haste, on December 12, 1774, asking if there was still time to add an explanatory note to the paper he had submitted "Sur la calcination des métaux dans les vaisseaux fermés." And he added:

Il m'importe que le Public soit convaincu, le plutôt possible, que je n'ai point l'intention de m'approprier le travail d'autrui;

166

& je suis convaincu que la delicatesse en Litterature & en Physique n'est pas moins essentielle qu'en Morale. Quoique l'experience du Pere Beccaria diminue de quelque chose la nouveauté de mes expériences, je vous avouerai cependant que sa Lettre m'a fait un tres-grand plaisir.[15]

Rozier had no difficulty in including Lavoisier's note (and indeed Lavoisier's letter to him) in the December, 1774, number of his journal. Lavoisier's note is followed by the passages from Beccaria's letter and the sentences in which Cigna summed up Beccaria's experiments. These last were evidently translated from the Latin of the *Mélanges,* as Lavoisier indicates, for the wording differs slightly from the French version in Rozier's journal.

This episode, together with Lavoisier's failure to mention Cigna in the *Opuscules,* makes it seem very likely that Lavoisier had not read Cigna's mainly physiological paper; he seems to have had his attention drawn to it more than two years after it had appeared in Rozier's journal. Yet I believe that even if he had read it, the paper would not have had the effect on him that Meldrum imagined, for neither Hales nor Cigna—and this is especially true of Cigna—really understood that air combined with burning phosphorus or sulphur!

To be sure, Hales had quite clearly stated in the *Vegetable Staticks* that two grains of phosphorus when burned "absorbed" on one occasion three cubic inches of air and at another time twenty-eight cubic inches; and he recorded

---

[15] *Observations sur la physique,* 4 (1774), 452. The letters of Beccaria and Lavoisier and the passage from Cigna are reproduced in *Oeuvres de Lavoisier—Correspondance,* II, 461–462 and 465–467. The letter of the Comte de Saluces was published for the first time by M. Fric (*ibid.,* pp. 431–433).

that when he ignited a large match made of linen rags dipped in melted sulphur, the burning match absorbed "198 cubick inches, equal to $\frac{1}{10}$ part of the whole air in the vessel." [16] Yet Hales, as Lavoisier was later to point out,[17] leaves the reader somewhat confused as to what actually takes place. There are passages, like those just quoted, where he seems to suggest that the burning solid or its vapor really absorbs and fixes air during combustion, thus decreasing the volume of air in the vessel. Elsewhere, however, he clearly states his opinion that the shrinkage in volume is due to a weakening of the elasticity of air. This elasticity, he writes, appealing to the authority of Isaac Newton, "is supposed to consist in the active aerial particles repelling each other with a force which is reciprocally proportional to their distances." [18] Air charged and clogged with vapors loses this elasticity and so shrinks in volume. The vapor of such burning substances as sulphur powerfully attracts the elastic particles of air:

And therefore the Candle and Matches ceasing to burn, soon after they are confined in a small quantity of air, seems not to be owing to their having rendred that air effete, by having consumed its *vivifying spirit;* but should rather be owing to

[16] Exper. CIII, pp. 226–227. Cf. *ibid.,* Exper. LIV, p. 169, and Exper. LXXVI, pp. 182–183.

[17] "M. Hales a encore remarqué que le phosphore ou plûtôt le pyrophore de M. Homberg diminuait le volume de l'air dans lequel on le brûlait. . . . Quant à la diminution du volume de l'air qui s'opère pendant la combustion de quelques corps, tantôt il l'attribue à la perte de son élasticité, tantôt il semble croire que cet air est réellement fixé et absorbé pendant la combustion, et son ouvrage semble laisser quelque incertitude à cet égard" (*Oeuvres de Lavoisier,* I, 459).

[18] *Vegetable Staticks,* Exper. LXXXIX, p. 207.

the great quantity of acid fuliginous vapours, with which that air is charged, which destroy a good deal of its elasticity, and very much clog and retard the elastick motion of the remainder.[19]

It is probable, then, that when Hales referred to the shrinkage of air volume in these experiments as an absorption of the air, he was using a mere shorthand expression to describe the appearances. This is certainly true of Cigna, who relies heavily on Hales but is somewhat more explicit in interpreting the chemical events.[20] In the passage which so impressed Meldrum, Cigna writes that two grains of phosphorus, lighted and enclosed in a container, absorb twenty-three inches of air. But this is evidently only a manner of speaking, for he explains immediately afterwards: "Les flammes diminuent le ressort de l'air, *non en l'absorbant,* mais en exhalant des vapeurs qui diminuent la force répulsive des parties de ce fluide avec lesquelles elles se mêlent." [21]

Though Hales (and Cigna after him) had clearly shown that the volume of air in which phosphorus or sulphur are burned diminishes as a result of the combustion, their explanations may well have seemed confusing to others besides Lavoisier. There was, however, one fact which, if it had been known and considered in the light of this phenomenon, could not but have set investigators

[19] *Ibid.,* Exper. CXVII, p. 273. It should be pointed out that Hales had found a *decrease* in weight of burnt phosphorus before it had run *per deliquium.* See below, note 22.

[20] "Dissertation de M. Cigna, sur les causes de l'extinction de la lumière d'une Bougie, & de la mort des Animaux renfermés dans un espace plein d'air," *Introduction aux observations,* II, 84–105.

[21] *Ibid.,* p. 97. The italics are mine.

on the right track. This was the observation that both sulphur and phosphorus increase markedly in weight when they are burned. Marggraf, who, as we have seen, first described phosphoric acid and the production of flowers of phosphorus, had noted, but not successfully explained or adequately emphasized, that when this substance is produced by burning phosphorus freely in air it is markedly heavier than the starting material. Rather surprisingly, this observation was not mentioned by Macquer in the article on phosphorus in his *Dictionnaire*, though he treated Marggraf's work at great length.

Sage, in his *Elémens de minéralogie docimastique*, made a similar but less precise observation. He mentioned the production of phosphorus by reduction of the acid and the reverse reaction by which phosphorus left exposed to the air is converted into a colorless, transparent acid weighing three times as much as the phosphorus. He noted the familiar deliquescent property of the acid and remarked that it weighed considerably more than the starting material. Attributing all or most of this increase in weight to the addition of water from the air, he estimated that one part of acid combines with at least two parts of water.[22] Meldrum suggested that this passage in the often speculative book of Sage may have influenced Lavoisier, perhaps first arousing his interest in phosphorus or calling

[22] *Elémens de minéralogie docimastique* (ed. 1772), p 5. Cf. Hales: "When 3 grains of *Phosphorus* were weighed, soon after it was burnt, it had lost half a grain of its weight; when two grains of *Phosphorus* was weighed, some hours after it was burnt, having run more *per deliquium* by absorbing the moisture of the Air, it had increased a grain in weight" (*Vegetable Staticks*, Exper. LIV, p. 169).

170

his attention to the greater weight of the phosphoric acid.[23] Lavoisier certainly knew the book,[24] for his name was mentioned by its reviewer, probably Rozier himself, in the April issue of the *Observations sur la physique;* [25] and in a later paper on the analysis of mineral waters Lavoisier seems to be referring to Sage when he expresses doubt that "a modern author" is correct in asserting that phosphoric acid belongs to the mineral realm and therefore that its salts are to be found in mineral waters.[26] But there is no reference to the production of phosphoric acid or to the increase in weight. I doubt whether Sage's rather confused observation, in which the hygroscopic properties of the acid obscured the more significant weight change when the phosphorus turns into acid, had any influence on Lavoisier, as most authors, following Meldrum, have claimed.

[23] Meldrum, *loc. cit.,* pp. 15–16.

[24] There is no record that Lavoisier owned a copy of this book, though he possessed the two-volume second edition of 1777, for it is recorded in the inventory of 1793 (Biblio. de l'Arsenal, 6496) and in the "Bibliothèque de Madame la Comtesse de Rumford," Tome I, Catalogue, p. 70. That Lavoisier owned the second but not the first edition of Sage's work suggests that it was the appearance of the expanded edition of 1777 that led Lavoisier to refute Sage's views concerning phosphorus in a paper he read in that year to the Academy (*Oeuvres de Lavoisier,* II, 139–152). If this is true, the value of Lavoisier's paper as evidence for Sage's presumed influence in 1772 is diminished to the vanishing point.

[25] The reviewer wrote: "Il semble que l'Auteur auroit dû citer le travail de M. Lavoisier sur le gypse, aussi instructif pour le fond, que satisfaisant pour ses résultats" (*Introduction aux observations,* II, 53).

[26] "Mémoire sur l'usage de l'esprit-de-vin dans l'analyse des eaux minérales," *Oeuvres de Lavoisier,* II, 29–37.

At least as likely a source for this significant piece of information is a brief reference in a book Lavoisier knew well: Guyton de Morveau's *Digressions académiques.* Here, in the same essay in which he announced the general fact of the increase in weight of calcined metals, Guyton recorded that when he ignited twenty-two grains of phosphorus by gentle heating in a retort he found the resulting product to be fifteen grains heavier.[27] Guyton worked with phosphorus as Lavoisier was later to do: that is, he prepared the "flowers of phosphorus" by burning, rather than by the slow, spontaneous combustion of phosphorus in air, the method that Sage employed; and he therefore realized that the absorption of water could not be mainly responsible for the gain in weight. Evidently unaware of Marggraf's observation, Guyton was later to claim credit for this discovery, though at the time its significance escaped him, as well it might in view of his theories about calcination.[28]

Be that as it may, there is no real evidence that any of this work—the paper of Cigna, the book of Sage, or the observation of Guyton de Morveau—drew Lavoisier's attention to the study of phosphorus or to the problem of combustion. We have seen that he came to study combustion by another route, through his interest in the cal-

---

[27] *Digressions académiques,* p. 252, note 1. This passage was first noted by Max Speter. See *Chemisch Weekblad,* 28 (1931), 80–81; also *Chemiker-Zeitung,* 55 (1931), 994. Speter even claimed that by having the memoir of October 20, 1772, initialed Lavoisier was seeking to assure himself priority over Guyton, as well as over Priestley and Mitouard. This is doubtful.

[28] Guyton wrote: "J'avois observé en 1772, que le phosphore acquérait une augmentation de poids sensible en passant à l'état d'acide" (*Encyclopédie méthodique—Chimie,* I (1786), 629.

cination and reduction of metals. In all likelihood he was impelled to study phosphorus, not by anything he encountered in his reading, but by a purely routine episode of academic business; or so at least the evidence would suggest.

Lavoisier and Mitouard

It will be recalled that our earliest trace of Lavoisier's interest in combustion and the first reference to his experiments on phosphorus are supplied by the note of September 10, 1772, discovered and printed by Meldrum in 1932.[29] This recorded the purchase of a sample of German phosphorus from the Parisian pharmacist, Pierre-François Mitouard or Mitouart, whose name has appeared several times in this narrative. I believe, though what I shall have to say is necessarily conjectural, that it was a memoir of Mitouard on phosphorus, which Lavoisier agreed to referee for the Academy of Sciences, that drew his attention to this substance and led to his now-classic experiments of the autumn of 1772.

That Mitouard's work on phosphorus was the starting point of Lavoisier's classic investigations was first strongly urged by Max Speter in a suggestive, but ill-fated and somewhat ill-considered, article published in 1926.[30] Speter was the first to point out that Mitouard read to the Academy in the fall of 1772 a paper that dealt with the products obtained by distilling phosphorus; at the same time he

[29] See above, pp. 6–8.
[30] Speter, "Kritisches über die Entstehung von Lavoisiers System," *loc. cit.*, pp. 578–582. Three years later Speter presented this theory unchanged and at length in *Das Buch der grossen Chemiker,* I, 313–316.

called attention to the report on this memoir submitted by Lavoisier and Macquer under the date of December 16, 1772.[31] Speter emphasized that in the document Lavoisier had singled out as "très-remarquable" Mitouard's passing observation that the weight of the phosphoric acid produced was greater than that of the "poudre phosphorique" from which it was prepared, and that he had called special attention to Mitouard's suggestion that this phenomenon was due either to the humidity of the air *or to the air itself.* Speter was further impressed by the striking resemblance, the *frappante Ähnlichkeit,* of this passage to the first sentence of Lavoisier's sealed note of November 1 (in which Lavoisier attributed the increase in weight of sulphur and phosphorus to the "prodigious quantity of air" that is fixed during combustion).

Speter knew—from a reference made by Berthelot— that Lavoisier had begun his work on phosphorus on September 10; but he did not know, though the fact would have interested him extremely, that Lavoisier purchased his first sample of phosphorus from this same

[31] First published in Rozier's journal in 1774 under the title: "Rapport fait à l'Académie des Sciences par MM. Macquer & Lavoisier, d'un Mémoire de M. Mitouard, dans lequel il s'est proposé d'examiner différentes substances qui se trouvent dans les vaisseaux où l'on distille le phosphore par le procédé de M. Margraff [*sic*], & que l'on a coutume de rejetter, quoiqu'il fût encore possible d'en tirer parti" (*Observations sur la physique,* 3 [1774], 421–423). It was reprinted with minor changes, an abbreviated title, and the addition of a first paragraph restating part of the longer title, in *Oeuvres de Lavoisier,* IV, 141–143. This new paragraph makes it clear that Lavoisier was the author of the report, for it begins: "L'Académie nous a chargés, M. Macquer et moi, de lui rendre compte, etc."

Mitouard, for on this point Berthelot was silent. Speter was not troubled by the circumstance that the report of Lavoisier and Macquer was dated as late as December 16; in spite of this fact, he was convinced that Lavoisier had seen Mitouard's memoir before October 20, perhaps as early as September; and he argued that the memoir of October 20—which at this time he knew only by hearsay —had been *paraphé* by Fouchy to ensure Lavoisier priority with respect to Mitouard's suggestion. In a later paper (1931) [32] Speter felt impelled to modify his view after learning from Paul Dorveaux, of the Academy of Sciences in Paris, that Mitouard's memoir had not been submitted officially until December 12, 1772, the very day the memoir was read to the Academy. [33] In consequence, Speter altered his hypothesis to suggest that Lavoisier and Macquer had prior knowledge of the contents of Mitou-

[32] Speter, "Lavoisierana," *loc. cit.*, p. 994, note 17. In a paper published the following year, in which he printed for the first time (anticipating Meldrum by several months) Lavoisier's outline memoir of October 20, Speter is less explicit in his claims for Mitouard. Here he writes: "Warum und wem gegenüber diese Prioritätssicherungen Lavoisiers? Er selbst gab in seinem, vermutlich 1792 verfassten, nach seinem Tode von seiner Witwe veröffentlichten historischen Rückblick auf seine epochalen Arbeiten über Metallverkalkung an, dass er sich gegenüber den englischen Gelehrten (Priestley!) das Eigentum an seiner Entdeckung sichern wollte. Verschiedene Indizien wiesen widerum auf eine Art Themenbesitzergreifung gegenüber dem Pariser Apotheker-Chemiker Mitouart und dem Dijoner Advokaten-Chemiker Guyton de Morveau hin." He makes no comparison between the content of Mitouard's paper and Lavoisier's memoir ("Die entdeckte Lavoisier-'Note' vom 20. Oktober 1772," *loc. cit.*, p. 107).

[33] Paul Dorveaux, "Quelques mots de plus sur Mitoüart," *Revue d'histoire de la pharmacie*, 19 (1931), 245–260.

ard's memoir, else it would be hard to understand how they could have rendered their report in the brief space of four days after Mitouard presented it.

In 1932 A. N. Meldrum—who seems to have seen only Speter's paper of 1926—strongly attacked the idea that Mitouard could have influenced Lavoisier. This he did chiefly on the ground that, by assuming the memoir to have been "held back for months whilst Lavoisier made illicit use of it," Speter was reflecting in a manner that was "wanton and deplorable" on the Academy of Sciences, its Secretary, and on Lavoisier himself. Nor was Meldrum ready to believe that Mitouard—a man he described as of no real eminence, not mentioned by Poggendorff or Kopp, and whose work consisted of mere "idle speculation"—could have been the source of Lavoisier's inspiration. Any similarity between Lavoisier's November note and Mitouard's speculations could, he contended, just as well prove that Lavoisier had influenced Mitouard as show the reverse. Meldrum's most telling argument was that Mitouard did not read his memoir to the Academy until December 12 (a fact Speter did not know in 1926); and this, Meldrum insisted, must have been soon after he completed his experiments, for Mitouard "had ready access to the *Académie*," and on two occasions the previous spring had presented to the Academy the results of experiments carried out only a few days—on one occasion only two days—earlier.[34]

Meldrum's arguments seem to have struck most scholars

[34] "Lavoisier's Three Notes on Combustion," *loc. cit.*, pp. 24–27. Meldrum also remarked that Mitouard, in contrast to Lavoisier, "worked with a derivative of phosphorus." This is not quite accurate; there is no evidence that Meldrum had read Mitouard's memoir; he probably judged it from Lavoisier's summary.

as conclusive; Speter's theory has been totally neglected by the more recent students of Lavoisier's work, perhaps because of Meldrum's attack, perhaps from a reluctance of French and English historians of chemistry to read the German literature. Nobody until now has seen fit to mention, let alone re-examine, the theory of the possible influence of Mitouard on Lavoisier. Yet with Speter's conjecture consigned to oblivion, we are left with the unexplained coincidence of Lavoisier's purchase of the phosphorus sample from Mitouard in September and his authorship of a report on Mitouard's phosphorus experiments on December 16, events which neatly bracket the period of Lavoisier's own classic experiments on the same substance.

Although I certainly do not accept Speter's theory, even as he eventually modified it, and cannot believe that Lavoisier had the note of October 20 initialed in order to ensure himself of priority with Mitouard specially in mind, the impression is unavoidable that there is some connection between Mitouard's rather crude investigations and the brilliant discoveries of Lavoisier. The sticking point is, of course, the late date at which Mitouard presented his results to the Academy. Although we can no longer believe, as Speter for a time did, that the Academy delayed for several months before reporting on a memoir that had been officially submitted to it, is it not possible that Lavoisier and Macquer knew of the contents of the memoir and perhaps had it in their possession as early as late August or the beginning of September? There are reasons to think that this may have been the case. Meldrum was not struck, as Speter was, by the significant fact that the Lavoisier-Macquer report was dated only four days after Mitouard had submitted his memoir to the Academy; yet this seems a surprisingly short time for these conscientious scientists to have reviewed it with care. Nor did Meldrum note (as Speter had done in his paper of 1931) that Lavoisier and Macquer, on the same day that they reported on the phosphorus paper, submitted reports on two other memoirs of Mitouard, memoirs which had been read to the Academy the previous spring and which had apparently suffered just the sort of delay Meldrum felt was intolerable to imagine. All this is suggestive, but hardly persuasive.

More convincing, I believe, are certain important similarities that can be observed between the language of Lavoisier's "memoir-torso" of October 20 and that of Mitouard's paper. These are more striking than the resemblances Speter thought he discerned between Lavoisier's note of November 1 and the Lavoisier-Macquer report on Mitouard's memoir. Neither Speter nor Meldrum seems to have looked at Mitouard's unpublished paper, though it could readily have been consulted in the archives of the Academy of Sciences. Such a comparison is quite revealing.

Though not a major contribution to science, Mitouard's investigation is a respectable piece of work that does not deserve Meldrum's harsh condemnation.[35] Mitouard's purpose was not to theorize about the production of phosphoric acid but to investigate the by-products left behind when phosphorus was prepared by what he described as

[35] "Examen de plusieurs substances qui se trouvent dans les vaisseaux ou l'on distille le phosphore que l'on rejette comme inutile quoiqu'il soit possible d'en tirer un bon parti. Par M. Mitoüard." This manuscript, thirteen pages in length, in Mitouard's own hand, is preserved in the archives of the Academy of Sciences.

178

Marggraf's laborious and costly method. He had observed that when the crude phosphorus prepared from urine was purified by distillation, in the final step of this process, there was a marked loss of material. Some of the missing phosphorus he felt might be recovered from the reddish-brown scales that adhered to the neck of the distillation flask or from the reddish powdery mass that collected in the bottom of the receiver. The scales, we can now see, were chiefly composed of the red allotropic form of phosphorus, which Mitouard seems to have been the first to describe; and the powdery material was probably impure phosphorus pentoxide mixed with some of the red phosphorus. The latter he was able to separate, at least partially, as insoluble reddish particles by washing the flocculent powder with distilled water. To his own satisfaction Mitouard showed that both forms of this reddish material consisted of relatively pure phosphorus altered in some mysterious way. When he heated samples of this red phosphorus, they burned brightly and produced the familiar white sublimate which was rapidly converted into an acid liquor.

In his "memoir-torso" of October 20, Lavoisier describes the same substances, and in words that closely resemble Mitouard's. The red phosphorus, which appeared to Mitouard as "écailles d'un brun rougeatre" or as "cette poudre jaune orangée" is described by Lavoisier as having a "couleur jaune rouille de fer." It consists, said Mitouard, of "un phosphore avec le moins de principe inflammable possible," words which Lavoisier appears to echo when he writes that it is phosphorus "qui a perdu une partie de son principe inflammable." Of the acid liquor into which the white vapors are transformed, Mitouard wrote: "Cet acide est dans son genre ce qu'est l'acide sulphureux volatile à l'acide vitriolique pur." On evaporating it, "on la concentre au point de luy donner la consistence d'une gelée." Lavoisier, who worked more carefully and astutely, starting from his sample of pure phosphorus, set down a similar observation in his memoir. When he burned the phosphorus under a bell jar, he produced a white sublimate (the pentoxide), which he identified as phosphoric acid in an absolute degree of concentration, "tel à peu près que l'huile glaciale de vitriol."

The verbal parallels are too striking to be fortuitous. Even if two men might be led independently to describe similar appearances in similar terms, is it likely that they would *interpret* their observations in such identical fashion? Why should both men suggest that the red scales consisted of phosphorus that had lost some of its phlogiston? And if it is obvious why Mitouard could compare his concentrated phosphoric acid to oil of vitriol, it is less clear why Lavoisier should have applied this analogy to the solid pentoxide. Yet all this makes sense if Lavoisier was familiar with Mitouard's memoir before he set down his own findings late in October.

That this was the case is further suggested by a passage of the Lavoisier-Macquer report on Mitouard's memoir— the passage, indeed, which had so impressed Speter. Here Lavoisier wrote:

Ce qui nous paraît très-remarquable, c'est que, à quelque degré de concentration qu'on porte cet acide [Mitouard's liquid phosphoric acid], son poids est toujours supérieur à celui de la poudre phosphorique qu'on avait employée. M. Mitouard attribue ce phénomène à l'humidité de l'air ou à l'air lui-même contenu dans les vaisseaux où se fait la combustion.[36]

By the time he submitted his report (on December 16) Lavoisier had observed in the course of his own experiments the "phénomène singulier" that the concentrated acid (in his case, the pentoxide, not the liquid) was substantially heavier than the phosphorus that had produced it, even though a small quantity of the phosphorus had been converted into the inactive allotropic form. This increase in weight, he felt sure, must be due to the absorption of air. It is therefore surprising to find him referring on December 16 to this increase in weight as "très-remarquable," as he does when describing Mitouard's work. Either he was deliberately concealing his recently acquired knowledge (in which case he would have been wiser, if scarcely more ingenuous, to pass this point over in silence, rather than single it out for comment) or he had actually written the report on Mitouard's experiments before the true explanation of this weight effect had been proved to his satisfaction by the end of October. In the light of all the evidence, I am inclined to accept the second explanation and to believe that Lavoisier must have had Mitouard's memoir in hand before October, and even that he knew of its contents or of the character of Mitouard's results before he purchased his now-famous sample of phosphorus in early September. I think also that he must have completed his written report before, rather than after, he had carried out his own more significant experiments. Later, when Mitouard formally submitted his mem-

[36] *Oeuvres de Lavoisier*, IV, 142.

oir in December—or so I read the events—Lavoisier simply turned in, in his and Macquer's name, the unaltered report that he had written earlier, rather than rewrite it in the light of his newer information. This conjecture does something to explain, moreover, the curious speed with which the report was submitted.

One can only guess at what actually led up to these events, but I think it extremely likely, for reasons I shall try to make clear, that Lavoisier and Macquer were responsible for urging Mitouard to present his memoir to the Academy as soon as convenient after the Academy's autumn recess, which was regularly observed between early September and the *rentrée publique* of St. Martin's day, about the middle of November. They may have agreed in advance to referee the paper Mitouard was to present; and if so—since it was often the custom for the *rapporteurs* to repeat certain of the key experiments contained in a memoir submitted to the Academy for approval —it was perhaps for this purpose that Lavoisier, early in September, purchased the famous sample of German phosphorus from Mitouard. To give these conjectures any substance, we should have to show that Macquer and Lavoisier were in some manner closely associated with Mitouard, that they esteemed him as a chemist, and that there was some reason for encouraging him in this fashion.

The little biographical information we possess about this obscure apothecary was assembled through the diligence of Paul Dorveaux, whose findings we may summarize here.[37] Mitouard had been born in 1733, in

[37] On Mitouard see P. Dorveaux, "Le cervelet de Voltaire et les Mitouart," *Bulletin de la Société d'histoire de la pharmacie*, no. 44 (November, 1924), pp. 409–421. I have not chosen to

Beauchastel en Vivarais, the son of a salt-tax official (*contrôleur au grenier à sel*) of that town. After serving his apprenticeship as a pharmacist and passing the examination for the *maîtrise,* he took the master's oath on September 2, 1761, and purchased an apothecary shop in the rue de Beaune, which soon became one of the best in the quarter. Here in his laboratory he began, in November, 1766, a course of private chemical lectures, which he continued to give each winter for twenty years. He was obviously respected for his professional skill. The future aeronaut, Pilâtre de Rozier, was for a time his apprentice. And in 1777 Mitouard was chosen to be the pharmacist in attendance during the last illness of Voltaire, furnishing the medicines which had been prescribed for the expiring philosopher by the famous Dr. Tronchin. Mitouard embalmed the corpse, rather botching the job, as it turned out; and so he was able to take possession of Voltaire's brain, preserve it in alcohol, and display it in his shop for many years to the delight of curious visitors. In 1781 Mitouard was named demonstrator in chemistry at the newly founded Collège de pharmacie (where in fact he had lectured since its foundation in 1777) and taught there until his death at the age of 53 on September 11, 1786. He published almost nothing, which explains why Meldrum could not find him mentioned in the chief biographical and chemical reference works. But he was not, it turns out, as poor a chemist as Meldrum would have us believe.

As Speter emphasized in a footnote to his paper of 1931,

follow Dorveaux in his rendering (Mitoüart or Mitouart) of this chemist's name but have retained the more common spelling used by Rozier, by Dumas in the *Oeuvres de Lavoisier,* and by Speter and Meldrum.

Mitouard had been known to Macquer and Lavoisier for some time before September, 1772. Our forgotten pharmacist was one of those who, like Macquer and Lavoisier in August, 1771, had witnessed the destruction of the diamond by Darcet and Rouelle at the Jardin du Roi.[38] In March, 1772, Mitouard made his first bid for recognition by the Academy of Sciences by appearing before it to present the prospectus of a work he proposed to prepare, for the Academy's series on the arts and crafts, on the "Art du peintre vernisseur et doreur."

At this time Mitouard was following closely the investigations on the diamond being carried out in the spring of that year; in fact he skillfully repeated and extended some of the work and offered to pay the cost of further large-scale experiments, if Macquer and Lavoisier would perform them. It is particularly significant that he continued his association with these scientists during the summer of 1772. When the Academy formally gave permission for the use of their great burning glass, Mitouard was invited to take part in this project; [39] and the record indicates that Mitouard did in fact play the role of observer, if not of very active participant, in the burning glass experiments; for on August 29 he brought the workers samples of *safran de mars* (iron sulphide) and of diaphoretic antimony to

[38] See above, p. 82.

[39] Macquer (*Introduction aux observations,* II, 612–616) mentions only that he and Lavoisier had been invited by the Academy to join with Cadet and Brisson in these experiments. But Lavoisier tells us, in his manuscript account, that Cadet and Brisson "inviterent dans cette vue M. Macquer Lavoisier et Mitouard de Concourir a leur objet et ils convinrent entre eux de travailler de Concert a Ce grand ouvrage" (Lavoisier papers, dossier 72 J, fol. 1 verso).

be subjected to the heat of the Tschirnhausen lens. On October 7 Mitouard did even better and provided a ruby for the experiments.[40]

Mitouard's associates did not, quite evidently, share modern scholars' low opinion of his work, and they were right, at least as far as Mitouard's diamond experiments of the spring of 1772 are concerned. With Cadet—and using the same furnace and the same apparatus employed by the three principal collaborators—Mitouard attempted to distill diamonds, but without conclusive results. More successful were the experiments in which, following the earlier suggestion of Maillard, he sought to protect the diamond from the effects of heat by using various "intermediaries." These experiments were carried out in his own laboratory in the rue de Beaune in the presence of Macquer, Lavoisier, Cadet, and other members of the Academy.[41]

Taking three diamonds, he sealed one in an empty piece of clay pipestem, surrounded another by chalk in a second pipestem, and protected a third in the same manner with powdered charcoal. Each pipestem was then placed inside a nest of tightly closed crucibles. Forcing his furnace to a higher temperature than the others had used, Mitouard heated the diamonds strongly for three hours. At the end of the experiment the diamond in the empty pipestem and the one embedded in chalk were found to have lost their polish and the sharpness of their angles and had decreased in weight, whereas the diamond

---

[40] *Oeuvres de Lavoisier*, III, 301 and 320. Speter describes Mitouard's role as that of "passiver Spender von Versuchsmaterial" in these experiments. See *Das Buch der grossen Chemiker*, I, 314.

[41] *Introduction aux observations*, II, 112–116.

protected by charcoal remained totally unaffected. To exclude the possibility that the divergent results in the three cases might have been due to differences in the diamonds, he significantly varied the next experiment by interchanging the samples. The diamond that in the first experiment had been protected by charcoal was now surrounded with a powder of calcined hartshorn, the one he had embedded in chalk was placed in powdered charcoal, and the one that had been unprotected was put in powdered glass. As in the first experiment, only the diamond protected by charcoal emerged without alteration. From these results Mitouard concluded that although diamonds can be readily destroyed by strong heat if exposed to the air, when air is effectively excluded and when they are protected by substances like charcoal which contain much phlogiston, they can resist the heat of the furnace and indeed avoid any semblance of damage. Mitouard compared this behavior of the diamond with that of antimony and zinc, substances he knew to resist calcination if protected by powdered charcoal. There is no doubt that Mitouard strongly suspected that the destruction of the diamond was the result of a combustion.

Lavoisier and Macquer had nothing but praise for these experiments of Mitouard. Lavoisier gave a full and respectful account of them in his general summary of the work on the diamond.[42] And in the first of their reports, made to the Academy on December 16, Lavoisier and Macquer spoke approvingly of Mitouard's diamond experiments of the previous spring.[43] In their second report,

[42] *Oeuvres de Lavoisier*, II, 54–56.
[43] Dorveaux, "Quelques mots de plus sur Mitoüart," *loc. cit.*, pp. 256–257.

dealing with his memoir on phosphorus, they wrote as follows:

> Ce mémoire de M. Mitouard nous a paru contenir des observations très-intéressantes, propres à répandre de nouvelles lumières sur la nature du phosphore et de son acide; il y donne d'ailleurs un moyen simple et peu dispendieux d'obtenir l'acide de phosphore en abondance, en le combinant à la base du nitre, et le procédé ne manquera pas de faciliter les recherches de ceux qui voudraient faire une étude particulière de la nature de cet acide.[44]

The *rapporteurs* recommended that all three of Mitouard's memoirs be printed in the Academy's *Mémoires des savants étrangers*. Such publication, it should be remembered, often preceded or accompanied the election of candidates to membership in the Academy. It is of some importance for our reconstruction of these obscure events to learn that this was supposed to be the case here.

Almost certainly with the encouragement of Macquer and Lavoisier, Mitouard was at this time an active candidate for membership in the Academy of Sciences and was relying on the active support of the academicians who appreciated his work. Precisely at this time a place of *adjoint chimiste* fell vacant, as a result of Lavoisier's promotion, on August 29, 1772, from the rank of *adjoint* to that of *associé*. Paul Dorveaux pointed out that Mitouard's was one of seven names put up at the election, scheduled for December 23, 1772, to find someone to fill Lavoisier's vacant chair. Mitouard, it should be remarked, was not successful; instead, his fellow apothecary, Antoine Baumé,

---

[44] *Oeuvres de Lavoisier*, IV, 143.

for whom there was especially strong support, was chosen, with the young chemist Bucquet next in line.[45] Nor did Mitouard even have the consolation of seeing his memoirs published, as Lavoisier and Macquer had urged, in the *Savants étrangers*. But this is beside the point. What emerges is that Mitouard's appearance before the Academy on December 12 to read his memoir on phosphorus was clearly intended to further his candidacy, for this was to be voted on eleven days later. The strange procedure by which Lavoisier and Macquer reported so soon after December 12, not only on Mitouard's phosphorus memoir, but also on his earlier diamond papers, is at once easier to understand and clearly marks these men as at least to some extent supporters of Mitouard's cause.

To sum the matter up, I think it probable—though perhaps beyond the reach of solid proof—that after his promotion in August, 1772, Lavoisier encouraged Mitouard, with whom he had collaborated and whose work he esteemed, to take the necessary steps to convince the Academy of his worth. Mitouard would then have described to Lavoisier his work on phosphorus or even put the memoir, or a draft of it, in his friend's hands, so that

[45] Dorveaux quotes the *Procès-verbaux* as follows: "L'Académie ayant procédé, suivant la forme ordinaire, à l'élection de deux sujets pour remplir la place d'adjoint chymiste vacante par la promotion de M. Lavoisier, la Classe a proposé Mrs. Demachy, Baumé, Mitoüart, Le Veillard, Bucquet, Delisle et Laborie, entre lesquels les premières voix ont été pour M. Baumé et les secondes pour M. Bucquet." See his "Quelques mots de plus sur Mitoüart," *loc. cit.*, p. 257. The Macquer correspondence reveals that the Duc d'Ayen, though not yet an *honoraire* of the Academy, sought to round up support in favor of Baumé's election. But Macquer was doubtless already inclined to favor his old associate. See Macquer correspondence, Bib. nat. MS Fr. 12305, I, nos. 31–34.

he could study it, repeat certain of the experiments, and have a report in readiness. Thus, even though Mitouard could not present the memoir much before the election—for the Academy would be closed during the annual autumn recess—the customary formalities could be quickly satisfied soon after the reconvening of the Academy in mid-November. As far as I can see, this reconstruction has at least the merit of accounting for most of the mysteries and peculiarities of the Mitouard episode.

Speter argued that Mitouard's casual suggestion that the addition of air might explain the greater weight of phosphoric acid led Lavoisier to embark for the first time on the study of combustion. My own interpretation is somewhat different. I think it may have been by some such train of events as I have proposed that Lavoisier was brought to investigate phosphorus. Perhaps, too, Mitouard's casual aside led him to explore the role of air in the combustion of this substance. But, as I have tried to show in this study, Lavoisier already had more than a faint suspicion, when he embarked on the phosphorus experiments, that the chemical participation of air could explain the analogous phenomenon of the gain in weight of calcined metals and the effervescences observed when they are reduced. He had already leaped the important and difficult mental hurdle—a hurdle raised and sustained by the widespread prejudice that air could not be a chemically significant substance—and he was probably chafing to get his hands on the Tschirnhausen lens to test his conjecture in the case of minium. The accident of having to evaluate Mitouard's work on phosphorus, perhaps stimulated by Mitouard's remark about the possible role of air, gave Lavoisier the unexpected opportunity as well as the incentive to explore an interesting possibility: namely, that what he believed to take place in the calcination and reduction of metals might also be true, as Mitouard seemed to think possible, in the case of burning phosphorus, a substance, incidentally, that could be readily studied without the use of the burning glass.

The course of events would then have been different from that which Lavoisier seems to describe in the sealed note of November 1 and this, I am persuaded, was the case. At the very beginning of these experiments on phosphorus, as the note of September 10 makes clear, Lavoisier set out to discover whether phosphorus absorbed air when it burned. As even Meldrum remarks: "It is noteworthy that he aimed, not at making a discovery, but at the verification of what had been reported." [46]

Whether Lavoisier saw Mitouard's memoir before September or whether he merely learned of Mitouard's speculations from casual conversation, it is likely that Lavoisier seized upon the suggestion that air might combine with burning phosphorus. We have seen that this passing suggestion made a deep impression on him. But this clue could only have fanned into flame a spark already aglow in Lavoisier's active mind. As I have tried to show, it was not Mitouard's memoir, still less the references by Sage, Cigna, or Guyton de Morveau to the odd behavior of phosphorus, nor even the experiments on the diamond, which first set him on the path to his great experiments on combustion. By his own testimony Lavoisier was led in the first instance to speculate about the nature of chemical

[46] "Lavoisier's Three Notes on Combustion," *loc. cit.*, p. 19. Meldrum, of course, had in mind the passages in the writings of Cigna and Sage.

effervescence, especially those effervescences observed when metallic calxes are reduced; but it was the remarkable experiments of Guyton de Morveau on the calcination of metals and Hales's theory of fixable air, now more significant in the light of the rumors that were beginning to circulate about new British discoveries of the same sort, that came together in his mind to suggest the hypothesis he proposed to test with the burning glass. It seems, therefore, to have been a mere accident that this hypothesis was first confirmed with phosphorus and then with sulphur, rather than by the experiment on the reduction of metallic calxes which he had envisaged as early as August 8, 1772.

Conclusion

LET me review briefly the argument that has been set before the reader in the course of this study. My purpose was to discover, if possible, how Lavoisier came to perform the famous experiments on the combustion of phosphorus and sulphur and the reduction of lead oxide which mark the beginning of his great creative period of chemical investigation. To this end I have examined with particular care the thinly documented period of Lavoisier's life just before he set down his three notes on combustion in the fall of 1772. I have considered, and I believe disposed of, some earlier conjectures (of Meldrum and others) about the origin of the experiments Lavoisier described in those notes. I have tried to re-create the state of chemical knowledge in the France of 1771–1772 insofar as it had a bearing on Lavoisier's work and have sought the influences which could have changed, and I believe did change, the direction of his thought; and I have tried to identify the accepted beliefs and prejudices which prevented others from thinking as he came to think.

Before 1772, indeed before the summer of that year, Lavoisier displayed no interest in the problem of combustion, in the calcination of metals, or in the chemistry of phosphorus. Nor had he given any thought to the possible participation of air in chemical reactions. The memorandum Lavoisier set down on August 8, 1772, which I have used so extensively, and his newly discovered "Système sur les élémens" of about the same date, are the earliest documents we possess in which Lavoisier mentions the chemical role of air. I have tried to show that this idea could not have been the result of any familiarity with the work of Joseph Black or Henry Cavendish or with Joseph Priestley's "Observations on Different Kinds of Air." The principal if not the sole source of Lavoisier's suspicions about air was Hales's *Vegetable Staticks*. Yet it was just at this time that the first intimations of the work of the later British pneumatic chemists came to the attention of French scientists, mainly as a result of the activities of J. H. de Magellan and Trudaine de Montigny. The first document of some significance to attract attention in France was Priestley's modest *Directions for Impregnating Water with Fixed Air*, published in the early summer of 1772 and soon thereafter translated into French. The information supplied by this pamphlet, the activity it aroused among the chemists of Paris, perhaps also the realization that Priestley was hard at work on more significant problems related to fixed air, probably explain why Lavoisier took pains to assure his priority for the experiments he performed in September and October, 1772.

Lavoisier's August memorandum, furthermore, contains valuable hints as to the origin of Lavoisier's work on combustion. These hints are confirmed, in part, from reminiscent statements Lavoisier made later in life. Stemming from his curiosity about effervescences, the problem that concerned him particularly in the summer of 1772

193

was the calcination of metals and the reduction of their oxides, not combustion in the broader sense nor the behavior of phosphorus. He was led to speculate about the effervescences observed when metallic calxes are reduced; and because of his knowledge of the work of Hales he attributed these effervescences to the release of air. He may have observed this reduction phenomenon directly, but it is more likely that he found it described in the chemical literature.

This phenomenon of effervescence, I feel sure, came to be linked in Lavoisier's mind with the fact that metals all increase in weight when they are calcined, a fact that had attracted renewed interest in 1771–1772. The generality, and even the reality, of the augmentation effect had long been doubted by many chemists. That the effect was real and observable with all calcinable metals was first clearly demonstrated by the Dijon chemist, L. B. Guyton de Morveau, in results submitted to the Academy of Sciences in Paris in the summer of 1771 and published in the late spring of 1772 in his neglected book, the *Digressions académiques*. I have found evidence for Lavoisier's knowledge of, and debt to, the experimental results of Guyton de Morveau.

But Guyton's fanciful phlogistic explanations of the augmentation effect seemed highly unsatisfactory. Doubtless by combining in his mind the fact of the gain in weight and his suspicion that metallic effervescences are caused by the escape of air, Lavoisier was led to interpret the weight increase of metals on calcination as due to the addition of air. As early as August of 1772 he had envisaged an experiment to test this hypothesis.

Indirect support for my reconstruction of Lavoisier's

train of thought is supplied by the letters Turgot wrote to his friend, the young Marquis de Condorcet, in 1771 and 1772. In one of these Turgot adduced the evidence of Hales's experiments (showing that air is found fixed in many solid and liquid substances) in support of his theory —identical with Lavoisier's—that Guyton's results could best be explained by the chemical combination of metals with air. Turgot, who anticipated Lavoisier by about a year, never published his theory or carried out experiments to confirm it, though his disclosure to Condorcet may have stimulated B. G. Sage and Condorcet late in 1772 to design an experiment to see if fixed air is given off from lead oxide. It is possible that Turgot's theory was known to Lavoisier before August, 1772, but there is no evidence that this was the case.

Lastly, I have attempted to understand why Lavoisier's demonstration of the role of air in combustion was first carried out by burning phosphorus and not—as he had evidently planned in August—by seeing whether air is given off when lead oxide is reduced. Though in some details my concluding chapter is admittedly more conjectural than the rest of this study, I have revived there in modified form an early suggestion of Max Speter. I believe that Lavoisier was obliged to postpone his projected experiment on lead oxide until he could have the exclusive use of the Academy's burning glass, with which he and his older collaborators had been experimenting during the summer and early autumn. In the interval he agreed to examine and report on a memoir on phosphorus submitted to the Academy by the pharmacist Mitouard, a man with whom he had worked closely. I do not believe that the possible chemical role of air was first suggested to Lavoisier by the sentence in Mitouard's memoir of which Speter made so much. Nor do I believe that Lavoisier had the summary of his own phosphorus experiments initialed at the Academy in order to gain priority over Mitouard. But it is possible—indeed, I think, likely—that Mitouard's suggestion that the increase in weight of burned phosphorus might owe something to the air may have led Lavoisier to investigate with this little known substance the possibility that had occurred to him in connection with metals. If Lavoisier, in the first instance, planned to confirm his suspicion by an experiment on the reduction of lead—and I have marshaled considerable evidence to show that he did—then the question of Lavoisier's interest in phosphorus, and the whole Mitouard episode, are both diminished in significance.

APPENDIX

I. EXPERIMENTS ON THE DIAMOND *

RÉSULTAT de quelques expériences faites sur le Diamant, par MM. MACQUER, CADET & LAVOISIER, lu à la Séance publique de l'Académie Royale des Sciences, le 29 Avril 1772.

Il n'étoit plus permis de douter de la possibilité de faire évaporer le diamant à l'air libre par la violence du feu, d'après les expériences multipliées qui avoient été faites sur cette singulière substance. (Voyez le Cahier de Janvier). Ce fait avoit été annoncé en Angleterre par le célèbre Boyle. Il avoit été complettement démontré à Florence par le Grand Duc de Toscane, à l'aide du miroir ardent, & il avoit été confirmé en Allemagne par les expériences de l'Empereur François Premier, faites dans des fourneaux; enfin, des Chymistes François, M. Darcet, M. Macquer, M. Rouelle & M. Roux, avoient contribué par de nouvelles expériences, à établir de plus en plus cette vérité.

Ces expériences, en apprenant aux Chymistes un fait très-extraordinaire, leur laissoit encore une vaste carrière à remplir. En effet, l'évaporation du diamant se faisoit-elle par une véritable réduction de cette substance en vapeurs; en un mot, pouvoit-on la regarder comme une véritable volatilisation? ou bien étoit-ce une espèce de combustion, semblable à celle qu'on remarque dans le phosphore & dans quelques autres

* *Introduction aux observations*, II, 108–111.

substances, ou enfin, n'étoit-ce pas plutôt une espèce de dé-crépitation, une division extrême des parties du diamant, occasionnée par le contact d'un air froid, une volatilisation par trusion, pour me servir de l'expression des Chymistes?

La configuration du diamant, presque tout composé de lames appliquées les unes sur les autres, voyez pl. I, comme l'observe le Traducteur du Traité des Pierres de Théophraste, sembloit favoriser cette opinion: mais elle étoit contredite en même tems par les expériences de Boyle; & cette odeur âcre & pénétrante qu'il avoit sentie pendant l'opération, sembloit annoncer une véritable volatilisation: d'un autre côté, l'observation singulière faite par M. Macquer, cette espèce d'auréole ou de flamme qu'il avoit remarquée, sembloit annoncer une combustion; mais on pouvoit lui opposer l'opération de M. Darcet, faite dans des boules de pâte de porcelaine. Les circonstances de cette évaporation sembloient exclure toute idée de combustion & de trusion, & ramenoient le phénomène à l'effet d'une volatilisation ordinaire; c'est-à dire, à l'opinion de Boyle.

Telles étoient les incertitudes qui règnoient sur cette matière, & qui ne pouvoient être levées que par de nouvelles expériences. Le voeu de l'institution de l'Académie Royale des Sciences, étant que les objets de quelque importance soient traités en commun, nous avons cru, M. Macquer, M. Cadet & moi, ne pouvoir mieux remplir les sages vues de ses Fondateurs, qu'en associant nos travaux. Nous nous sommes assemblés en conséquence dans le Laboratoire de M. Cadet, pour tirer au clair, s'il est possible, cette matière encore obscure; & voici la manière dont nous avons raisonné.

Si le diamant est véritablement volatil, s'il peu se réduire en vapeurs sensibles, comme l'a observé Boyle, il est dès-lors possible de le soumettre à la distillation ou à la sublimation. Si, au contraire, le diamant n'est point volatil, & qu'il ne se détruise à l'air que par combustion ou par quelque effet méchanique de l'air, quelque feu qu'on lui fasse éprouver dans les vaisseaux fermés, il n'en doit point être alteré: de là, deux expériences à tenter; la première, de soumettre le diamant au plus grand feu possible dans des vaisseaux fermés; la seconde, de lui faire éprouver le même feu dans des vaisseaux distillatoires.

D'après ces vues générales, nous avons pris des diamans de toutes couleurs & de toutes qualités que nous avions rassemblés; ils étoient en petites pierres, dont les plus fortes pesoient environ demi-grain, poids de marc; le tout réuni, pesoit 19 grains 5/8 poids de marc: ces diamans ont été placés dans une petite cornue de grès bien saine, & qui avoit été enduite de terre; elle étoit adaptée à un récipient de verre auquel elle a été lutée avec du lut gras: on avoit seulement ménagé un petit trou au matras pour donner issue aux vapeurs, en supposant qu'il en sortit. La cornue a été mise à feu nud, dans un fourneau dont M. Cadet avoit plus d'une fois eprouvé l'effet dans l'essai des mines. On a d'abord échauffé lentement les vaisseaux; on a augmenté ensuite insensiblement la chaleur; enfin, on a donné trois heures d'un feu très-violent; au bout de ce tems, on a laissé refroidir les vaisseaux, & on les a délutés. Le recipient ne s'est trouvé contenir qu'un peu de vapeurs aqueuses, que ce lut avoit fournies. Par rapport à la cornue, elle étoit saine & entière; en la secouant, on entendoit encore les diamans sonner dans son intérieur. On les a obtenus sans peine, du moins la plupart, en retournant la cornue; & on les a vu tomber à-peu-près tels qu'ils avoient été mis: ils étoient seulement presque tous dépolis, & leur surface étoit recouverte d'un enduit brunâtre. L'intérieur de la cornue avoit acquis la même couleur; cette teinte même avoit pénétré dans quelques endroits jusques dans l'intérieur de sa substance, comme on pouvoit le remarquer dans les fractures.

Ces diamans ayant été reportés à la balance, ne se sont plus trouvés peser que 16 grains 6/32, au lieu de 19 grains

201

5/8; mais ayant cassé la cornue, on s'est apperçu que quelques diamans étoient demeurés au fond, & qu'ils y avoient été fortement attachés, par quelques portions de sable & de terre, que la violence du feu avoit ramollies & préparées à la fusion. Ces diamans pesoient environ 3/4 de grain, d'où l'on a conclu que la diminution de poids qu'avoient éprouvé les diamans dans cette opération, étoit de 2 grains 22/32, c'est à-dire, de près d'un septième de leur poids.

Quoique le feu donné dans cette opération fût supérieur à celui qui avoit été employé chez M. Rouelle pour l'évaporation du diamant à l'air libre, on pouvoit cependant encore craindre que le défaut d'évaporation ne tînt au degré du feu; & il étoit de la plus grande importance de lever toute sorte de doute à cet égard.

M. Maillard, habile Jouaillier, persuadé que le diamant ne s'évaporoit qu'autant qu'il avoit le contact de l'air libre, avoit apporté avec un zèle digne de la reconnoissance des Savans, trois diamans, dans l'intention de les soumettre à telle expérience qu'on jugeroit à propos; il consentoit qu'ils fussent tourmentés par le feu le plus violent, pourvu qu'on lui permît de les garantir du contact immédiat de l'air. M. Maillard fut en conséquence chargé de disposer lui-même ses diamans de la façon qu'il jugeroit à propos. Il les plaça dans une pipe à tabac, remplie de charbon pilé; cette pipe fut exactement fermée avec un lut composé de terre détrempée avec de l'eau salée; enfin, la pipe fut placée dans un creuset enduit de craie, lequel lui-même étoit contenu dans deux autres creusets abouchés l'un à l'autre; toutes les jointures étoient exactement lutées avec la même terre détrempée d'eau salée.

Le creuset ainsi disposé, après avoir été bien sèché, fut placé dans un fourneau où il essuya pendant deux heures un feu très-vif; cependant, comme on s'apperçut que les barreaux de la grille étoient un peu serrés, que d'ailleurs, l'ouverture supérieure du dôme n'étoit pas assez grande; qu'elle n'étoit pas proportionnée au volume du fourneau, on craignit d'avoir manqué le but de l'expérience, faute d'avoir donné le plus grand feu possible. Dans cette circonstance, M. Macquer proposa d'envoyer chercher un fourneau d'une construction particulière, qui donnoit un feu bien plus supérieur à tous ceux connus, & dans lequel il avoit fondu avec beaucoup de facilité, la pierre à chaux, le gypse & d'autres substances aussi réfractaires. La proposition fut acceptée avec reconnoissance; & en moins de deux heures, on fut en état de transporter le creuset d'un fourneau dans l'autre, avec toutes les précautions convenables. On donna, à l'aide de ce dernier fourneau, deux heures du feu le plus violent; après quoi, on jugea à propos d'arrêter, dans la crainte de fondre & le creuset & le fourneau. On laissa refroidir le tout pendant plusieurs heures, après quoi on tira le creuset du feu. Il étoit entièrement déformé; toute la craie & la terre qui servoient de lut, étoient vitrifiées & ne formoient qu'une masse; la seule pipe n'avoit point cédé à l'action du feu, elle avoit été seulement convertie en porcelaine, & faisoit corps avec les matières fondues, dont elle avoit été environnée; il ne fut plus possible de l'ouvrir qu'en cassant le gâteau.

Si-tôt que la pipe fut fendue, on en vit sortir & la poudre de charbon aussi noire qu'elle y avoit été mise, & les huit diamans; ils avoient encore leurs facettes, leur poli; en un mot, ils étoient tels qu'avant l'opération; ils avoient seulement pris une légère teinte de noir, qui ne paroissoit que superficielle. Ces diamans pesés ensemble ou séparément, donnèrent exactement le même poids qu'avant l'opération.

Comme il ne peut rester aucun doute sur la violence du feu donné dans ces expériences, elles prouvent d'une manière incontestable que le diamant n'est volatil qu'autant qu'il a le contact de l'air; que cet être, au contraire, est absolument fixe, lorsqu'il est exposé à la violence du feu dans des vaisseaux fermés & avec des précautions convenables, notamment lorsqu'il est environné de poudre de charbon; qu'enfin, si le diamant s'est évaporé dans les expériences faites en Angleterre, en Italie, en Allemagne & en France, ce phénomène ne doit point s'attribuer à une véritable volatilisation, comme on le pensoit; mais plutôt à une espèce de combustion, comme celle du charbon, & de quelques autres substances qui résistent, comme lui, à la violence du feu dans les vaisseaux fermés, ou bien que cet effet est dû à une réduction des parties du diamant en une poudre très-fine, occasionnée par le contact de l'air. Nous nous proposons de nous assurer, par de nouvelles expériences, à laquelle de ces deux opinions on doit s'arrêter.

II. LAVOISIER ON THE BURNING GLASS INSTALLATION *

Les experiences faittes Sur le diamant dans le laboratoire de M. Cadet par M. Maquer [sic] Cadet et Lavoisier. celles faittes depuis au fourneau de porcelaine de Seve [1] enfin Celles [que] M. Cadet et Mitouard y ont ajoute et qui ont eté lues a lacademie des Sciences et publiées commencent a repandre de la lumiere Sur la question interessant [sic] de la volatilisation ou plutot de la destruction du diamant par le feu mais il restoit encore plusieurs questions a decider Sur la nature de Cet effet.

M. Cadet—qui pensoit que la destruction de Cette pierre pretieuse netoit autre chose quune division extreme (des) de ses parties (du diamant) occasionné par le contact de lair une espece de decrepitation—Crut qu'un moyen Simple de

* Lavoisier papers, archives of the Academy of Sciences, Paris, dossier 72 J. A two-page draft in Lavoisier's hand, evidently intended as an introduction to the account of the burning glass experiments presented to the Academy of Sciences in the fall of 1772. I have retained Lavoisier's spelling and punctuation. Passages which Lavoisier crossed out are printed here in parentheses. My own queries and emendations are in square brackets.

[1] Seve = Sèvres.

Confirmer ou de detruire Son oppinion Seroit de repeter les experiences du grand duc de toscane a l'aide (du verre) d'un miroir ardent. il en confia le projet a M. Brisson et ils firent de concert avec un miroir de ———[2] pouces appartenant a ce dernier quelques experiences dans Cette vue. ils ne tarderent pas a s'appercevoir que leffet du miroir qu'ils employoient n'etoit pas Suffisant et le diamant quils y avoient exposé ne parut pas Sensiblement alteré. la necessité demployer un agent plus fort leur donna l'idee de Servir de la grande lentille (du palais royal) connue Sous le nom de lentille du (palais) palais royal (et qui) qui avoit passé depuis a M. Donsenbray[3] et qui faisoit partie du Cabinet quil avoit legué a lacademie

en Consequence le ———[4] juillet 1772 MM. Cadet et Brisson demanderent a lacademie la permission de tirer de Son Cabinet et la lentille et Sa monture ainsy que quelques autres instrumens qui paroissoient necessaires pour Cette operation, a la charge (de faire) dy faire les reparations necessaires a leur frais. lacademie ne pouvoit recevoir qu'avec acclamation leur proposition et tous les ordres necessaires furent donner en consequence.

(il ne sagissoit) M.M. Cadet et Brisson Sentirent Combien il etoit important de profitter de cette circonstance pour repeter tout ce qui avoit été fait par M.M. homberg et Geoffroy avec le verre ardent et pour y ajouter de nouvelles experiences il [sic] invitcrent dans cette vue M. Macquer Lavoisier et Mitouard de Concourir a leur objet et ils convinrent entre eux de travailler de Concert a Ce grand ouvrage.

[2] Lavoisier's omission.

[3] Louis-Léon Pajot, Comte d'On-sen-Bray or D'Onsenbray (1678–1754), government official and *honoraire* of the Academy of Sciences. He was famous for the collection of machines kept in his country house at Bercy and bequeathed to the Academy of Sciences.

[4] Lavoisier's omission.

il ne Sagissoit plus que de trouver une place commode pour y etablir la lentille (M. Brisson Crut devoir prendre a cet egard les ordres de M. le duc de la vrilliere.[5] Ce ministre voulut bien ecrire a M. Marchais gouverneur du Louvre) il etoit necessaire que lemplacement fut Suffisamment vaste pour y operer librement, que [la] disposition fut telle que le Soleil y fut visible pendant la plus grande partie de la journée et principalement deux heures avant midy et deux ou trois heures apres   enfin il falloit que lendroit choisi fut a une distance Convenable de chacun des academiciens qui devoient operer. une des Cours du louvre parut lendroit le plus propre a remplir ces differens objets. M. Brisson Se chargea (en ce) de prendre a cet egard les ordres de M. le duc de la vrilliere. Ce ministre voulut bien en ecrire a M. Marchais gouverneur du louvre et lui donna ordre de procurer aux academiciens toutes les facilites qui pourroient leur etre necessaires.

Les cours du louvre netoient pas exemptes de tout inconvenient 1° le batiment du louvre quelque position quon eut prise devoit necessairement masquer le Soleil de bonne heure en hiver 2° laffluence du monde pouvoit devenir incommode dans un lieu public et on ne pouvoit esperer dy jouir de la tranquillité necessaire pour bien operer. M. Marchais obvia a toutes ces difficultes de la maniere la plus honete en offrant aux academiciens le jardin de linfante pour en disposer a leur volonte le faire ouvrir et fermer toutes les fois quils le jugeroient apropos. Cette proposition fut accepte [sic] avec reconnoissance et les dispositions furent faittes pour S'etablir au jardin de l'infante. la monture du verre ardent ne laissoit pas que de faire une machine asses grande et asses embarassante on en pourra juger aisement par la description qui Se

[5] Louis Phélypeaux, Comte de Saint-Florentin and Duc de Lavrillière (1705–1777), Secretary of State for the Maison du Roi and in this capacity in charge of the royal academies.

trouvera a la Suitte. il falloit necessairement un hengard pour la renfermer et pour la mettre aux injures de lair les academiciens Convinrent den faire faire un a leurs depenses il etoit necessaire dobtenir a cet effet lagrement de M. de Marigny [6] il le leur accordat avec toute l'honneteté que son zele pour les Sciences est capable de lui inspirer.

M. Mitouard fut charge de Soccuper de la construction du hengard, mais M. de la ferte [7] et M. —— [8] ayant appris lobjet de la construction quon alloit entreprendre S'empresserent de fournier tous les bois necessaires, et le hengard fut Construit aux depens des menus plaisirs.

(tchirnausen avoit construit dans) independamment de la lentille du palais royal construitte par tchirnausen [sic] achette par Mr. le regent (la meme) Ce meme phisicien en avoit fait dans le meme tems une Seconde d'un foyer beaucoup plus court elle n'avoit que —— [9] de foyer tandis que Celle du palais royal en avoit [10]

Cette lentille (avoit) apres avoir passé par differentes mains ainsy quon le verra dans lhistoire détaillée que nous en donnerons etoit tombé entre les mains de M. le Compte [sic] [11]

---

[6] Almost certainly Abel François Poisson, Marquis de Marigny (1727–1781), the brother of Madame de Pompadour. He held the post of *Directeur Général des Bâtiments, Jardins, Arts et Manufactures du Roi*.

[7] Perhaps the "M. de la Ferté" listed in the *Almanach Royal* for 1772 as an official of the Bureau d'administration des dépenses de la Maison du Roi.

[8] Lavoisier's omission.   [9] Lavoisier's omission.

[10] Sentence left unfinished by Lavoisier.

[11] The manuscript breaks off at this point.

III. THE AUGUST MEMORANDUM *

REFLEXIONS Sur les experiences qu'on peut tenter a l'aide du miroir ardent

Du 8 Aout 1772 [1]

La theorie de Sthal Sur le phlogistique Et Sur la reduction des Metaux avoit été adopté en allemagne longtemps avant qu'il en eut été question en france. des 1697, ce Celebre Chimiste avoit exposé cette doctrine, et l'avoit mise dans tout Son jour dans Ses observations chimiques, Medicinales Et phisiques.

Ce n'est qu'en 1723 Epoque de la publication du Cours de chimie Suivant les principes de Sthal et de Neuton que les chimistes françois ont parlé pour la premiere fois des Experiences de Sthal. on Se persuadra difficilement cependant qu'une doctrine aussi celebrée en allemagne; aussi digne de l'etre, ait été tellement confinee pendant douze ans dans le lieu qui l'avoit Vu naitre, qu'il n'en ait rien penetré *dans les pays voisins et Surtout* en france. les doutes qu'on pourroit former a cet Egard, Se Convertiront presqu'en certitude lorsqu'on Remarquera la Conformité (frappante) des principes de M. Sthal Et de ceux Repandus dans les (Memoires) *ouvrages* de M. Geoffroy l'ainé. C'est principalement dans un memoire publié parmi ceux de l'academie pour l'année (1729) *1709* a l'occasion des Experiences qu'il avoit faittes (au Verre

* Lavoisier papers, archives of the Academy of Sciences, Paris.

The original is in a secretarial hand, corrected in numerous places by Lavoisier. The words and phrases he crossed out are here placed in parentheses; his emendations and additions follow in italics.

The date added on the first page beneath the heading is probably not in Lavoisier's hand. This is certainly true of the note appended to it, which seems to have been added at a later date.

[1] Lu à l'académie des sciences, le 19 Août 1772, sous le titre de *Mémoire Sur le feu élémentaire.* [This note appears in the MS.]

ardent) avec la lentille du palais Royal (que M. Geoffroy a exposé Ses idées Sur la Composition des metaux.)

(Les observations qu'il avoit faittes l'avoient conduit a conclure que tout Metal etoit composé,) *que Cette Conformité paroit plus frappante il y Conclud que tout metal ou Substance metallique est compose* 1.° d'une terre Vitrifiable, particulière a chacun deux. 2.° d'une huile ou d'un principe inflammable, le meme qui Se trouve dans Les Vegetaux, dans les animaux, dans le Charbon et il (avoit remarqué) *y fait observer* que cette Substance (pouvoit) *peut* Se Separer des Metaux, qu'on en (pouvoit) *peut* la leur Enlever, (Et) la leur rendre a Volonté, la faire passer d'un metal dans un autre, la prendre indifferemment dans les trois Regnes de la nature Et que dans tous les Cas elles Rend(oit) egalement au metal Son Eclat, Sa ductilité Et Ses autres proprietés.

il est aisé de voir que ce Sisteme ne differe de celui de Sthalh qu'en ce que M. Geoffroy appelle Matière huileuse ou Substance inflammable ce que M. Sthalh nomme phlogistique, or il faut avouer que meme aujourd'huy nous ne Connoissions pas encore asses bien la nature de ce que nous nommons phlogistique pouvoir rien prononcer de tres precis Sur Sa nature.

Soit que ce Sisteme fut celui de St[h]alh, Soit que M. Geoffroy en fut (L'auteur) l'inventeur Toujours est il Vrai que les experiences faittes au Verre ardent conduisoient a le former, Et cela Suffit pour faire Sentir combien Ce Genre d'experience est important.

L'action de ce feu Supérieur a celui que nous Employons dans nos laboratoires n'a encore été appliqué qu'aux Substances Metalliques, il n'a point été fait d'experiences Suivies Sur les terres, les pierres, les Mines, Et Sur une infinité de Substances Mineralles. (Enfin) encore le peu d'experiences (meme qui a été fait ne l'a ete qu') *qui nous ont ete transmises a t'il ete fait* a l'air libre Sans qu'on ait apporté aucune Variété dans les pro-

209

cedés. les experiences par le Verre ardent offrent donc encore une Carriere toute nouvelle a parcourir. *On S'en convaincra de plus en plus par les refflexions qui suivent.*

Le feu que les chimistes ont coutume d'employer ne peut S'allumer ni Subsister dans le Vuide. l'air est un agent necessaire a Sa conservation. le feu du Verre ardent offre a cet egard un tres grand avantage. il peut penetrer Sous le Recipient de la Machine pneumatique Et l'on peut par Son Moyen faire des Calcinations et des Combinaisons dans le Vuide.

On ignore Si le Cristal de Roche est absolument fixe au feu du Verre ardent, mais il est probable qu'il y Resiste: voilà donc une Matierre avec laquelle on pourra Construire des appareils distillatoires et Sublimatoires a l'aide desquels on poura Rassembler les Vapeurs Et la fumée qui S'élevent dans presque toutes les operations faittes au miroir ardent. Cette meme Substance fournira des creusets transparents dans lesquels on poura observer tous les progres de chaque experience.

Enfin le Verre ardent (est un Moyen de) *pourra servir a* porter le feu le plus Violent jusque dans le Sein des fluides. Et il en Resultera encore un Genre d'experiences absolument neuf.

d'apres Ces Vues Generales sur les Experiences qu'on peut tenter au Verre ardent, il Reste pour mieux fixer les idées a en faire L'application aux principales Substances que nous Connoissons. on Commencera par dire un mot des Supports.

DES SUPPORTS

Les Matierres que l'on a Regardé jusque ici comme les plus Refractaires, Sont le Caillou, l'agathe, le quartz, le cristal de Roche, le grais, la porcelaine Et les Coupelles faittes d'os Calcinés. ces Matieres Sont infusibles par tous les feux que nous Connoissons; Mais Resisteront elles au feu du Verre ardent? (c'est ce qu'on n'est pas encore en etat d'assurer, il y a neantmoins tous lieu de l'esperer.) (*on a tout lieu de l'esperer, mais on n'est*) on n'est pas encore en etat de l'assurer, mais on a tout *lieu de l'esperer.* on a cru devoir preparer en consequence a l'avance des Creusets de ces differentes Matierres, on S'est muni de petites Soucoupes d'agathe, on a Rassemblé des tessons de Cristal de Roche; meme de petits Vases en forme de Creusets. d'un autre Coté M. Macquer a fait faire a Seve [2] des especes de petites Coupelles de porcelaine Sans Couvercle; il (n') a eu Soin de n'introduire dans leur Composition que des terres tres Refractaires. Et on a tout lieu de Croire qu'elles Resisteront a la Violence (du feu) de la chaleur. on Se propose egalement de Se Munir d'un nombre Suffisant de Coupelles d'os Calcinés: Enfin on Choisira des pavés du grès le plus Compact, on les Creusera un peu dans leur milieu, Et on en espere encore un excellent Service.

EXPERIENCES A TENTER SUR LE DIAMANT

Le diamant est il Susceptible d'evaporation a l'air libre, ou bien Simplement de division, ou de décrepitation? est il absolument fixe dans les Vaisseaux fermés? a quoi tiennent les differences qu'on observe en raison des intermedes dans lesquels il est placé, ces questions Sont extremement importantes, on propose pour parvenir a les Resoudre 1°. de placer un diamant passablement gros dans le fond d'un Creuset profond de Cristal de Roche Et de l'exposer au feu du Miroir ardent Sans le Couvrir; Si le diamant n'est point Susceptible de Volatilisation, mais Simplement de decrepitation, il Se divisera en fragments tres minces qui Se retrouveront pour la plus part dans le Creuset de Cristal. il en passera bien quelques fragments par dessus les bords, mais cette quantité ne peut etre bien considerable Et la plus grande partie doit rester. Si au Contraire le diamant est Veritablement Volatil tout Se dissipera, on ne Retrouvera absolument rien dans le Creuset.

Si cette experience laisse encore quelques doutes, Si l'on craint que les eclats du diamant n'ayent passés par dessus

[2] Seve = Sèvres.

les bords du Creuset, pour prevenir toute objection, on le fermera avec une Couche legere (de) *de Pate de* porcelaine, on Sait que cette matierre est poreuse, Et n'empeche point la destruction, ou au moins l'eparpillement du diamant, mais elle Suffira pour empecher les particules les plus fines de passer par dessus les bords du Creuset.

Mais en Supposant que le diamant decrepite (est a ce) *est-ce au* Contact de l'air au Refroidissement Subit qu'est du le phenomene? pour le decouvrir on pourra placer Le diamant dans un petit Vaisseau de Cristal de Roche bien bouché, meme au milieu d'un balon de Verre exactement fermé Et dans lequel on aura fait auparavant le Vuide par la machine pneumatique, *et lui faire eprouver dans cet etat la chaleur du verre ardent.*

DES METAUX

Independamment des Experiences de M. Homberg Et de M. Geoffroy Sur les Metaux qu'il faudra repeter, il Sera bon d'essayer S'ils Se Calcinent dans les Vaisseaux fermés. tous donnent une Vapeur ou fumée par le Verre ardent, il Seroit tres interessant de trouver un appareil propre a la retenir Et a la condenser. des Vaisseaux de Cristal de Roche rempliroient cet objet, mais il faut S'assurer auparavant S'ils resistent a l'effet du Verre ardent.

DES PIERRES

Cette partie est celle qui offrira le plus Vaste champ d'experiences   on aura a repeter toutes les experiences de M. Pott, toutes celles de M. D'Arcet, Enfin toutes celles de M. Macquer. On Soupconne aujourd'huy l'on pourroit meme dire qu'il est presque prouvé que les pierres ne Sont autre chose que des Sels insolubles dans l'eau, la plus part d'apres ce principe (Sont) *doivent etre* composées d'un acide Et d'une base, le point important Seroit de (les decomposer) parvenir a les decomposer a (en) Separer l'acide Soit par la Violence du feu Soit par la

Voye de Combinaison; on pourra de meme que les Metaux essayer de les mettre en fusion dans les Vaisseaux fermés; Enfin chemin faisant on poura faire quelques Combinaisons propres a imiter le flind Glass, le Spath fusible, Et quelques autres pierres [qui] Sont extremement pesantes, peutetre que, combinés avec le Verre, elles lui donneroient le degré de *refringence* convenable.

Quelques experiences Sur des mines de fer, de plomb, d'argent etc. Sur la bleinde Et (autres) *Sur quelques autres* Substance Metalliques pourront (apprendre des choses neuves) *donner des lumieres* Sur la maniere d'etre des metaux dans ces Combinaisons.

DES FLUIDES

J'ai Vu quelque part, c'est je crois dans le journal enciclopedique, que Si l'on Reçoit les Rayons Solaires au milieu d'un grand bocal rempli d'eau, il Se forme au foyer du Verre une poussiere qui tombe au fond du Vase, Et que l'auteur attribue aux Rayons Solaires (meme) fixés dans cette experience. Rien n'est moins probable que ce fait cependant il est indispensable de le repeter.

Les liqueurs Spiritueuses ne S'enflamment que par le contact d'une flamme, un Corps en ignition, un Charbon ardent S'y eteint, il paroit que les Rayons Solaires brulent a la façon des Charbons Et ne font point l'office de flamme   Et c'est Sans doute pour cette Raison que l'esprit de Vin ne (S'en flamme) *S'allume* pas au Verre ardent. les experiences jusques ici n'ont été faittes qu'avec des instruments foibles, en Sera t il de meme avec le miroir du palais Royal, l'effet sera-t-il le meme Sur l'esprit de Vin, Sur l'Ether Et Sur toutes les liqueurs Spiritueuses.

213

SUR L'AIR FIXE, ou plutot,
Sur l'air Contenu dans les Corps.

Il paroit Constant que (la pluspart) l'air entre dans la Composition de la plus part des Mineraux, *des Metaux meme Et en tres grande abondance.* aucun chimiste Cependant n'a fait encore entrer l'air dans la definition ni des Metaux ni d'aucun corps mineral. une effervescence n'est autre chose qu'un degagement Subit de l'air qui etoit en quelque façon dissout dans chacun des Corps que l'on Combine.

Ce degagement a lieu toutes les fois qu'il entre moins d'air dans la Combinaison du nouveau Composé qu'il n'entroit dans chacun des deux Corps qui entrent dans la Combinaison. (on ne Suivra pas ces Vues plus loin. elles sont le Sujet d'un travail deja fort avancé meme en partie Redigé) *Ces vues Suivies et approffondies pourroient Conduire a une theorie interessante quon a meme deja ebauchée,* mais ce qui doit ici fixer l'attention, c'est que la plus part des Metaux ne font plus d'effervescence lors qu'ils ont ete tenus longtemps au feu du Miroir ardent. Sans doute que le degré de Chaleur qu'ils y eprouvent leur enleve l'air qui entroit dans leur Combinaison. ce qui est tres particulier, c'est que les metaux dans cet etat ne Sont plus malleables Et qu'ils Sont presqu'indissolubles dans les acides. cette observation qui a encore besoin de Confirmation peut fournir une ample matierre a observations Et a Reflexions.

il Seroit bien a desirer qu'on put appliquer au Verre ardent l'appareil de M. halles [sic] pour mesurer la quantité d'air *produitte ou absorbée dans chaque operation,* mais on craint que les difficultés que presentent ce genre d'experience ne Soit insurmontable au Verre ardent.

IV. *LAVOISIER'S SYSTÈME SUR LES ELÉMENS* *

ESSAY SUR LA NATURE DE LAIR
REFFLEXIONS SUR LAIR ET SUR SA COMBINAISON DANS LES MINERAUX

aoust 1772

Premiere

[on Scait a n'en pouvoir douter que lair entre pour beaucoup dans la Composition des mineraux]

une foule dexperiences paroissent prouver que lair entre pour beaucoup dans la composition des mineraux [S'il etoit possible den douter les refflexions Contenus dans ce memoire] Cependant ces experiences Semblent ignorées elles n'ont point ete liees a la theorie chimique et les chimistes modernes malgre les faits frappans quils avoient Sous les yeux [ont tojours] on laisse subsister les [memes] anciennes deffinitions quils avoient donne des mineraux ils ny ont point fait entrer lair. on n'a pas de nouvelles experiences a donner icy mais on a tache de rassembler celles qui existoient pour en tirer des Consequences quelques unes etoient peu connues dautres douteuses on a repetees les unes et les autres du moins pour la plus part et cest le resultat de Ce travail qu'on va donner aujourd'huy.

[il paroit quil entre peu dair dans la composition des acides mineraux [et vegetaux] au moins ne S'appercoit-on pas quils

* Reprinted from René Fric, "Contribution à l'étude de l'évolution des idées de Lavoisier sur la nature de l'air et sur la calcination des métaux," *Archives internationales d'histoire des sciences,* 12 (1959), 138–145. This issue of the *Archives* did not appear until the early months of 1960. M. Fric indicates all passages which Lavoisier crossed out by placing them in square brackets.

en fournissent Sensiblement dans les combinaisons une preuve de ce fait c'est qu'on peut [autant] donner a un corps quelconque la propriete de faire effervescence avec les acides ou lui enlever a volonte or si la propriete de

Seconde

faire effervescence residoit dans lacide [ce ne Seroit pas en] l'effervescence Seroit toujours la meme quelque changement queprouve la base

Avant daller plus loin cest icy le moment dexpliquer ce que nous entendons precisement par effervescence. leffervescence nest autre chose qu'un degagement Subit dair]

dans tout Combinaison de deux Corps on peut distinguer trois Cas ou les deux corps combines admettent autant dair dans leur Combinaison que chacun en admettent Separement ou bien ils en admettent plus ou enfin ils en admettent moins. dans le premier Cas le mélange se fait paisiblement [Sans] dans les deux autres au contraire il y a ou absorption dair ou degagement dair.

Ce que nous venons de dire relativement a lair on peut le dire également du phlogistique ou de la matierre du feu. toutes les fois que dans une Combinaison les deux Corps combines admettent plus de matierre du feu dans leur Combinaison que chacun nen admettoit Separement il y a absorption de matierre du feu et refroidissement Si au contraire [il y] ils en admettent moins il y a degagement de la matierre du feu et par consequent chaleur.

la chimie fournit des exemples frequents de Ces degagemens ou de ces absorptions dair et de la matierre du feu

La combinaison des acides mineraux avec la Craye fournit un volume dair cent trente fois plus grand que celui de la Craye qui avoit ete employe

Troisième

en Sorte quen Supposant [que tout lair dans cette operation]

comme il est tres probable que tout lair fournit dans cette operation appartienne a la craye il S'en suivra que Cette Substance
contient pres de moitié de Son poids dair.

tous les acides [fournissent] Combines avec les alkalis fournissent egalement une grande quantite dair a moins que ces
memes alkalis nayent ete depouilles de leur air par des operations particulieres Comme on le verra dans la Suitte de Ce
memoire

Les metaux Sont encore dans le meme cas cest au moins ce
quon observe [dans un grand nombre de Circomstances] com-
munement dans leur melange avec les acides [par rapport]

Par rapport aux combinaisons qui absorbent de lair elles ne
Sont pas plus rare le melange de la chaux avec leau Celui de
Cette meme Substance avec [une grande] le Sel ammoniac
[absorbent enormement dair, il en est de meme de la Combinaison de lacide vitriolique] enfin la decomposition du Sel marin
par lacide vitriolique et la Combinaison de Ce meme acide avec
la chaux absorbent une quantite dair extremement considerable

on peut [encore suivre cette meme] Suivre encore icy l'ana-
logie [Sur le degagement et lassorbtion de la matierre du feu
dans les Combinaisons] de lair et de la matierre du feu et faire
voir quil y a Similitude dans les effets

il y a telle [union de Corps qui Se fait avec chaleur comme]
combinaison ou il y a effervescence avec chaleur Comme dans
[toutes les combinaisons] lunion

Quatrieme

des [lacide] acides avec lalkali *vegetal* et la terre calcaire

dautres combinaisons Se font avec effervescence et reffroidissement cest a dire avec absorbtion de la matierre du feu
comme lunion des acides avec lalkali marin [base de la Soude]
ou avec les alkalis volatils [et peut etre plusieurs la dissolution
de presque tous les sels dans leau enfin] un troisieme ordre de
Combinaison Se fait Sans effervescence mais avec refroidissement tel Sont les Solutions de presques tous les Sels dans leau

enfin un quatrieme ordre [de comb] Se fait Sans effervescence et avec chaleur tel est melange de lesprit de vin [a leau] et de lhuille de vin a l'eau

[on pourroit demander a Cette occasion pourquoi le melange des Sels avec la glace reffroidit]

aoust 1772
Cinquieme

REFFLEXIONS SUR LA COMBINAISON DE LA MATIERRE DU FEU DANS LES CORPS

on peut demander icy par quel raison le melange des Sels avec la glace produit plus de froid que leur melange avec l'eau

javoue que je ne Sens pas parfaittement lexplication de ce phenomene mais voicy Comment je le concois

il faut une certaine quantite de fluide *igné* pour communiquer a leau la chaleur de leau bouillante il faut une quantite dautant moindre de ce meme fluide que leau approche davantage du terme de la congellation. Supposons pour un moment [1]

Sixieme

on peut encore demander icy pourquoi toute evaporation est accompagne de reffroidissement, je repondrai [que] qu'une evaporation nest autre chose qu'une combinaison dune matierre quelconque avec la matierre du feu. cest donc icy le Cas dune Combinaison avec absorbtion de matierre du feu et par consequent le cas du reffroidissement

qu'un vase plein deau Soit sur le feu leau Se combine avec la matierre du feu [et] elle devient équiponderable a lair dans [cet etat] et par consequent volatile.

S'il ny a pas reffroidissement dans ce cas dans leau restante dans le vase Cest que le feu lui rend a mesure la quantite de matierre du feu quelle perd meme en plus grande quantite la meme chose arrive a toute evaporation toute leau du vase en

---

[1] The rest of this page is blank.

218

evaporation retrouve par la Communication de tous les Corps environnans [tout] la quantite de matierre du feu que levaporation lui enlève.

il nen est pas de meme lorsque par des moyens [forces on produit une evaporation rapide] forces tels que lagitation on produit une evaporation rapide alors la quantite de matierre du feu qui est enlevée ne pouvant etre asses Subittement fournie par les Corps environnants il [Se trouve] en resulte un reffroidissement necessaire.

Septieme

Ces explications nous Conduisent insensiblement a concevoir la matierre du feu dans deux états dans la nature 1° Comme combinée avec les autres elemens et [avec tous les corps Comme on lobserve egalement de lair] peut etre avec tous les corps de la nature a differente dose tel quest a peu pres l'air 2° Comme un fluide Stagnant qui penetre les porres de tous les Corps [et] qui Se met a peu pres en equilibre dans chacun deux et dont [labsen] la plus ou moins grande intensité produit les differens degres de chaleur.

aout 1772

Huitieme

Apres avoir expose le jeu de l'air et de la matierre du feu [il reste a parler de la maniere d'etre de l'eau dans] dans la composition des corps, il reste a parler de la maniere [detre de l'eau] dont lcau cntrc dans Ccs mcmes Combinaisons et principalement [dans latmosphere] de la maniere dont elle existe dans latmosphere.

[L'eau s'unit a la matierre du feu et dans cet etat]

Leau [dans la nature] est Continuellement penetrée par le fluide ignée comme tous les Corps de la nature plus ce fluide est abondamment mele avec l'eau plus il ecarte les parties plus il la dilate leau nest donc aproprement quun melange du fluide aqueux et de matierre du feu dans differentes proportions [Sui-

219

vant quelle est plus] et ce sont ces memes proportions que nous exprimons quand nous disons que l'eau est plus ou moins chaude.

Si par le moyen du feu artifficiel nous parvenons a Combiner la matierre du feu avec leau dans une proportion plus forte Si nous [unissons] environnons la molecule deau de molecules [dair au point d'eau] de feu alors Ce fluide entre en expansion il forme des vapeurs et dans Cet état il forme un fluide tres analogue a l'air.

Neuvieme

le feu tient infiniment peu a [Cette] leau dans Cette combinaison la preuve cest que [Si lon present] Si on presente [a Ce fluide] a l'eau ainsy reduitte en vapeurs un corps froid cest a dire qui [aye peu de matierre d] Soit peu penetre de matierre du feu, il S'y unit et le penetre jusqua Ce quil Se Soit mis en equilibre alors leau Cesse dexister en vapeur elle redevient eau. Ce mechanisme est Celui qui a lieu dans toute distillation [ainsy distiller nes autre chose que de] le liquide contenu dans la Cucurbite Surchargée de matierre du feu devient equiponderable a l'air il S'élève dans le chapiteau mais a mesure quil le touche Cette meme matierre du feu qui tend a Ce mettre en equilibre dans tous les corps [y passe] le penetre et leau qui na pas comme elle la propriete de penetrer le verre ou le metal dont est Compose lalembic reste a la surface interieure du chapiteau Sy rassemble en goute et coule le long de la goutierre et du tuyeau.[2]

[L'eau qui ne Se dissout quavec peine dans lair y devien tres]

toute evaporation de l'eau ou dun fluide quelconque etant

[2] A note in the margin at this point reads as follows: Ce fluide se dissout dans lair [parce que] et la matierre du feu reste unie a l'eau voila donc un fluide nouveau combine avec lair explication du refroidissement par evaporation evaporation par lelectricite nouveau fluide.

220

due a la Combinaison de Ses parties avec Celles du feu il Sen Suit que dans toute evaporation il doit y avoir absorption de matierre du feu comme on a vu plus haut quil arrivoit dans quelques Combinaisons et par Consequent reffroidissement et

Dixieme

cest ce qui arrive en effet. on Scait que Si lon trempe la boule dun termometre dans un fluide evaporable elle baisse Sur le champ de plusieurs degré et dautant plus que la liqueur est [plus evaporable] plus evaporable nest-il pas evident que dans Cette experience levaporation du fluide [nest] est faitte aux depends de la matierre du feu [de tous les corps environnans et du corps auquel elle touche il en prend probablement dans lair environnant mais il en] contenu dans le thermometre plus vous accelereres levaporation plus vous absorberes de matierre du feu plus aussy vous produires de froid.

L'eau combiné avec le feu forme un nouveau fluide trcs ana-logue a l'air avec lequel neanmoins il ne se mele point mais dans lequel il peut Se dissoudre jusqua Saturation (voyes Ce que j'entens par dissolution) il paroit que dans le vuide [leau en etat de vaporisation fait en tout office de l'air] la combinaison de leau et de la matierre du feu est durable et que ce fluide en vaporisation fait en tout office dair. il paroit même Certain que Si latmosphere aerée qui entourre notre globbe etoit detruite il S'en reformeroit une autre analogue qui Seroit composee deau en vapeurs.

quoi quil en Soit il nen nest pas moins Certain que l'eau en vapeurs nest point miscible a lair. Si dans un recipient vuide dair on introduit quelques gouttes deau et quon les reduise en vapeurs elles le rempliront comme feroit de veritable air mais

Onzième

Si en meme tems on rend lair au recipient aussitost leau en vapeurs qui nest [Soluble quen petite] point miscible a l'air et qui ne S'y dissout quen petite quantite est pour la plus grande precipitée elle Se dépose en goutte Sur les parois interieurs du [ballon] recipient par rapport a la matierre du feu elle rentre dans les corps environnans [dans lesquels] elle y produit une augmentation momentanée de chaleur laquelle ne dure que jusquau moment ou lequilibre est retablie.

leau en vapeurs est soluble dans lair en petite quantité mais dans des proportions données premier etat dans lequel l'eau existe dans latmosphere.

Douzieme

SUR LES EFFERVESCENCES FROIDES
MEMOIRES ACAD 1700 p. 110

M. Geoffroy a fait voir que beaucoup de melanges qui occasionnent des effervescences produisent du froid

les alkalis volatils meles avec les acides donnent du froid

[les alka] l'alkali fixe vegetal donne du chaud

on Scait aujourdhuy que le feu entre dans la composition de tous les Corps. Si dans une combinaison de deux corps il y a degagement de matierre du feu autrement dit si les deux Corps reunis ont moins danalogie avec la matierre du feu Si la quantite necessaire a la combinaison est moindre il y a degagement de matierre du feu

Treizième

[Si le mélange] Si les deux corps combines au contraire en ont plus besoin quavant la combinaison ils en absorbent ils en enlevent aux corps environnans ils doivent donc être plus froids

REFFLEXIONS SUR LAIR

aout 1772

*Quatorzième et de*re

Mais comment lair existe-t'-il dans les Corps Comment Ce fluide Susceptible dune Si terrible expansion peut il Se fixer dans [les corps et y] un Solide et y occuper un espace six cent fois moindre quil n'occupoit dans l'atmosphere. Comment concevoir que le meme corps puisse exister dans deux etats Si differens.

La Solution de Ce problem tient a une theorie Singuliere que je vais essayer de faire entendre cest que lair que nous respirons nest point un etre simple Cest un fluide particulier combine avec la matiere du feu [je ne p.] je prie le public de me pardoner Si jentre dans des details un peu long [mais le principal objet est detre clair dailleurs quand il] pour lamener a mon oppinion toute idée neuve demande une espece de preparation pour etre admise et je suis oblige [moi me] pour me faire entendre de Conduire le lecteur par la route que j'ay Suivi moi meme dans mes idées

voyes mes idées Sur les elemens

Le 19 Aoust 1772 M. Lavoisier m'a presenté [La] present [modèle] mémoire pour estre paraphé ce que Jay fait et le luy ay rendu

Defouchy

V. THE NOTE OF SEPTEMBER 10 *

EXPERIENCES SUR LE PHOSPHORE DU 10 7BRE 1772

j'ay achette chez M. Mitouard une once de beau phosphore venant d'allemagne quil m'a laissé a 45 Livres prix de la facture

j'en ay mis un petit morceau dans une bouteille le phosphore est devenu lumineux il a fumé mais Sans chaleur Sensible. je l'ay aproché du feu Sur le champ il s'est enflammé avec petillement la phiole a medecine ne Sest pas cassé

* Lavoisier papers, archives of the Academy of Sciences, Paris. This truncated note appears in the small green notebook entitled "Analise de differentes eaux," p. 38.

enhardi par Ce Succes jay voulu par Ce meme appareil veri-
ffier Si le phosphore absorboit de l'air dans Sa Combustion j'ay
lié avec un fil bien Serre une vessie au Col de la bouteille dans
laquelle j'avois introduit auparavant 15 grains de phosphore
j'avois fait un autre petit trou a la vessie pars le haut et j'en
avois exprimé tous l'air le trou de la vessie ayant ete bien [1]

VI. THE DRAFT MEMOIR OF OCTOBER 20, 1772 [*]

Memoire Sur lacide du Phosphore et Sur Ses Combinaisons
avec differentes Substances Salines terreuses et metalliques.

Si l'on expose du phosphore a l'aire libr il S'eneleve Continuellement une emanation ou (vapeur invisible) fumée peu
Sensible pendant le jour lumineuse (pendant la nuit) dans
l'obscurité. Cette vapeur nest autre chose qu'une petite portion
dacide unie a beaucoup de phlogistique et Si lon parvient a la
rassembler par le moyen dune cloche de verre ou par un autre
appareil quelconque on la reconnoitra pour un esprit volatil
acide de phosphore.

Le Contact de lair libre est necessaire pour Cette operation
parceque la vapeur du phosphore en Se convertissant en esprit
volatil acide de phosphore absorbe une (quantite considerable)
petite portion dair de Sorte quil est prouve que lair entre
naturellemen dans la composition de ce mixte et quil Sy Combine et quil Sy fixe de la meme maniere quil arrive dans un
grand nombre de Combinaisons chimiques.

Si au lieu de laisser le phosphore Se consommer a lair libre on
le met a Sec et Sans eau dans un vaisseau fermé de peu de
Capacité

[1] The manuscript breaks off at this point.

[*] Lavoisier papers, archives of the Academy of Sciences, Paris,
dossier 1308 D. Parentheses indicate passages crossed out by Lavoisier; square brackets, my own emendations.

Enfin Si on communique au phosphore un degre de chaleur un peu Superieur a lEau bouillante il s'enflamme tranquillement en donnant une belle flamme accompagne [sic] dune fumée epaisse le phosphore Se decompose le phlogistique labandonne une (portion) quantite extremement considerable dair est absorbée et Se combine avec la vapeur blanche

Si l'on rassemble la vapeur ou fumée par le moyen dun [sic] cloche ou autrement on obtient une espece de Sublimé blanc qui nest autre chose que lacide du phosphore dans un degré de concentration absolu et tel a peu pres que lhuille glacialle de vitriol. ces fleurs ou Sublimé Se resolvent en quelques heures et par la Seule humidite de lair en un acide tres puissant Sans odeur et qui presente a peu pres la meme apparence que lhuille de vitriol

un phenomene Singulier cest que (lacide) la quantite dacide retirée du phosphore par Cette derniere operation est ponderiquement plus grande que la quantite de phosphore meme qui l'a produite. Cette augmentation de poids (quil nest pas aisé de) dont il nest pas aisé de Constater au juste la (quantite) proportion provient de la combinaison de lair qui Se fixe dans Cette operation

la totalite du phosphore ne Se decompose pas par la combustion. il en reste toujours une petite portion au fond de la Capsulle qui ne Senflamme plus. elle est de couleur jaune rouille de fer. Cette petite portion nest autre chose qu'un phosphore qui a perdu une partie de Son principe inflammable il ne Sagit pour lobtenir dans Son premier etat que de le distiller avec des matierres inflammables.

je decrirai a Cette occasion la methode dont je me Suis Servi pour obtenir une grande quantite dacide du phosphore cette methode na dautre inconvenient que detre longue et ennuyeuse   du reste elle est Sure et (la perte est) la dissipation de lacide est presque nulle.

j'ay pris un grand plat de fayence emaillé au milieu du quel j'ay place une petite capsule dagathe. et j'ay recouvert le plat avec une tres grande cloche de verre. javois prealablement introduit dans la cloche un peu deau distillée affin (quelle fut) que les vapeurs Se Condensassent avec plus de faciliter. j'ay ensuitte mis un petit morceau de phosphore dans la capsulle dagathe et je l'ay enflammé avec la pointe dun couteau (et) echauffe a la flamme d une bougie. Ce Phosphore en brulant donnoit une vapeur blanche tres epaisse qui Circuloit dans la cloche. mais il nen Sortoit que tres peu au dehors par la raison qu une quantite asses considerable dair etant absorbé dans Cette operation lair exterieur qui entre a mesure dans la cloche pour le remplacer fait refluer les vapeurs en dedans au lieu de les faire Sortir

(Lorsque j'avois fait deux ou trois Combustions) il falloit environ une heure pour (absorber) fixer la totalite des vapeurs

apres quoi je recommençois   mais il etoit necessaire au bout de quelques experiences de reimbiber la cloche ou deau distillee ou dacide foible.

a la fin de chaque Combustion il reste au fond de la Capsulle une petite portion de phosphore de couleur jaune rouille de fer telle quon l'a decritte plus haut.

Cette maniere dobtenir lacide du phosphore est la meme a peu pres que Celle quon employe pour faire lhuille de vitriol

on observe pour le Souphre comme pour le phosphore que si lon chauffe peu et que Si lon brule lentement on obtient un esprit volatil tandis quau contraire par une combustion plus vive on obtient un acide Concentré

On peut encore obtenir dune autre facon une assez grande quantite dacide phosphorique   on prend un grand ballon ou matras (on y jette un) quon laisse debouche   on y jette un petit morceau de phosphore puis on fait chauffer a la flamme dune bougie lendroit du ballon qui touche immediattement au phosphore il Senflamme donne une vapeur blanche qui sattache aux parois interieurs du vase. il faut employer tres peu de phosphore dans cette experience attendu quon ne peut obtenir dacide quen proportion de la quantite dair que contient le vase. Sil y a plus de phosphore que lair nen peut decomposer il Se sublime sans bruler.

on Seroit tente de croire au premier coup doeuil que lair exterieur doit rentrer dans le ballon a mesure quil est absorbe par la vapeur de lacide et entretenir ainsy la combustion du phosphore   mais il en arrive autrement. les vapeurs qui Se forment dans le ballon font loffice dair elles en remplissent la capacite et empechent lacces de celui qui est exterieur au ballon

Le 20 Octobre 1772. Le présent écrit Contenant Cinq pages m'a été présenté par M. Lavoisier pour estre paraphé ce que J'ay fait et le lui ay rendu à L'Instant à paris Les Jour et an que dessus

DE FOUCHY

VII. THE SEALED NOTE OF NOVEMBER 1, 1772 *

Le présent écrit a été [déposé] remis entre mes mains cacheté par M. Lavoisier Le 1er Novembre 1772 pour estre déposé au Sécrétariat, ce qui a été fait et ouvert en presence de Lacade dans L'assemblée du 5 May 1773 à la requisition de L'auteur qui a demandé La présente mention pour luy Conserver sa date

DE FOUCHY

il y a environs huit jours que j'ay decouvert que le Souphre en brulant loin de perdre de Son poids (en brulant) en acquieroit au contraire; Cest a dire que d'une livre de Souphre on pouvoit retirer beacoup plus dune livre dacide vitriolique, abs-

* *Oeuvres de Lavoisier—Correspondance*, II, 389–390. I have corrected Mr. Fric's printed version in a few insignificant points after comparing it with the original in the archives of the Academy of Sciences.

traction faitte de lhumidité de l'air. il en est de meme du phosphore. Cette augmentation de Poids vient dune quantite prodigieuse d'air qui Se fixe pendant la combustion et qui Se Combine avec les vapeurs.

Cette decouverte que j'ay Constaté par des experiences que je regarde Comme decisives m'a fait penser (ce) que Ce qui Sobservoit dans la Combustion du Souphre et du phosphore pouvoit bien avoir lieu a l'egard de tous les Corps qui acquierrent du poids par la Combustion et la Calcination et je me Suis persuadé que laugmentation de poids (de l) des chaux metalliques tenoit a la meme Cause. lexperience a Complettement Confirme mes Conjectures. j'ay fait la reduction de la litharge dans les vaisseaux fermés avec lappareil de M. hales et j'ay observé qu'il Se (produisoit) degageoit au moment du passage de la chaux en metal une quantite Considerable dair et quelle formoit au moins un volume mille fois plus grand que la quantite de litharge employé [sic]. Cette decouverte me paroit une des plus interessantes qui ait ete faitte depuis Sthal et Comme il est difficile de ne pas laisser entrevoir a Ses amis dans la Conversation quelque chose qui puisse les mettre Sur la voye de la verité j'ay Cru devoir faire le present depost entre les mains de M. le Secretaire de lacademie (pour) en attendant que je rende mes experiences publiques

fait a Paris le 1er novembre mil Sept Cent Soixante douze

LAVOISIER

VIII. THE MEMORANDUM OF FEBRUARY 20, 1773 *

Avant de commencer la longue suite d'expériences que je me propose de faire sur le fluide élastique qui se dégage des corps, soit par la fermentation, soit par la distillation, soit enfin par les combinaisons de toute espèce, ainsi que [sur] l'air absorbé dans la combustion d'un grand nombre de substances, je crois

* M. Berthelot, *La révolution chimique—Lavoisier*, pp. 46–49.

devoir mettre ici quelques réflexions par ecrit, pour me former a moi-même le plan que je dois suivre.

Il est certain qu'il se dégage des corps dans un grand nombre de circonstances un fluide élastique; mais il existe [plusieurs] systèmes sur sa nature. Les uns, comme M. Hales et ses secta-teurs, ont pensé que c'était l'air lui-même, celui de l'atmosphère, qui se combinait avec les corps, soit par l'opération de la végé-tation et de l'économie animale, soit par des opérations de l'art. Il n'a pas pensé que ce fluide put être différent de celui que nous respirons, à la différence qu'il est plus chargé de matières nuisibles ou bienfaisantes, suivant la nature des corps dont il est tiré. Quelques-uns des physiciens qui ont suivi M. Hales ont remarqué des différences si grandes entre l'air dégagé des corps et celui que nous respirons, qu'ils ont pensé que c'était une autre substance, à laquelle ils ont donné le nom d'air fixe.

Un troisième ordre de physiciens ont pensé que la matière élastique qui s'échappe des corps était différent [sic], suivant les substances dont il avait été tiré, et ils ont conclu que ce n'était qu'une émanation des parties les plus subtiles des corps, dont on pouvait distinguer une infinité d'espèces.

Un quatrième ordre de physiciens [sic]

.   .   .   .   .

Quelque nombreuses que soient les expériences de MM. Hales, Black, Magbride [sic], Jacquin, Cranz, Pristley [sic] et de Smeth, sur cet object, il s'en faut bien néanmoins qu'elles soient assez nombreuses pour former un corps de théorie com-plet. Il est constant que l'air fixe présente des phénomènes très différents de l'air ordinaire. En effet, il tue les animaux qui le respirent; tandis que celui-ci est essentiellement nécessaire à leur conservation. Il se combine avec une très grande facilité avec tous les corps; tandis que l'air de l'atmosphère, dans les mêmes circonstances, se combine avec difficulté et peutêtre ne se combine point du tout. Ces différences seront développées dans toute leur étendue, lorsque je donnerai l'histoire de tout ce qui a été fait sur l'air qu'on dégage des corps et qui s'y fixe. L'importance de l'objet m'a engagé à reprendre tout ce travail, qui m'a paru fait pour occasionner une révolution en physique et en chimie. J'ai cru ne devoir ne regarder tout ce qui a été fait avant moi que comme des indications; je me suis proposé de tout répéter avec de nouvelles précautions, afin de lier ce que nous connaissons sur l'air qui se fixe, ou qui se dégage des corps, avec les autres connaissances acquises et de former une théorie. Les travaux des différents auteurs que je viens de citer, considérés sous ce point de vue, m'ont présenté des portions séparées d'une grande chaîne; ils en ont joint quelques chaînons. Mais il reste une suite d'expériences immense à faire pour former une continuité. Un point important que la plupart des auteurs ont négligé, c'est de faire attention à l'origine de cet air qui se trouve dans un grand nombre de corps. Ils auraient appris de M. Hales qu'une des principales opérations de l'économie animale et végétale consiste à fixer l'air, à le combiner avec l'eau, le feu et la terre, et à former tous les [corps] combinés que nous connaissons. Ils auraient encore vu que le fluide élastique qui sort de la combinaison des acides, soit avec les alcalis, soit avec toute autre substance, vient encore originairement de l'atmosphère; [ce] dont ils auraient été en état de conclure, ou que cette substance est l'air lui-même, combiné avec quelque partie volatile qui s'émane des corps, ou au moins que c'est une substance extraite de l'air de l'atmosphère. Cette façon d'envisager mon objet m'a fait sentir la nécessité de répéter d'abord et de multiplier les expériences qui absorbent de l'air, afin que, connaissant l'origine de cette substance, je pusse suivre ses effets dans toutes les différentes combinaisons.

Les opérations par lesquelles on peut parvenir à fixer de l'air sont: la végétation, la respiration des animaux, la combustion, dans quelques circonstances la calcination, enfin quelques combinaisons chimiques. C'est par ces expériences que j'ai cru devoir commencer.

INDEX

Academy of Dijon, 125, 126, 127, 129
Academy of Sciences (Paris), 1, 5, 61, 62, 73, 75, 82, 85, 92, 93, 96, 109, 115, 119, 143, 147, 153, 173, 175, 176, 185, 195, 196
Black's work mentioned, 14, 18, 69
Demachy's paper read, 17
Magellan's association with, 36
Trudaine de Montigny, *honoraire* of, 42
Macquer, *associé chimiste* of, 45
letters of Magellan read, 53, 58-59
Venel's memoirs read, 66
Bucquet's experiments reported to, 72
Darcet's memoir read, 79, 81
séances publiques of, 87, 182
prize contest of, 120
Guyton's *Dissertation* presented to, 136-138, 194
cabinet of curiosities, 157
Tschirnhausen lens of, 157-158, 195
Mitouard's relations with, 176-178, 182, 184, 187-189
report of Lavoisier and Macquer to, 186
Acidum pingue, 16, 48
Admiralty, Lord Commissioners of the, 56
Aerial niter, 21, 118
Aerial particles, mutual repulsion of, 168
Affinity, 142, 149
Air, 3, 4, 5, 19-21, 27, 32, 52, 54, 65, 67, 71, 72, 82, 84, 87, 88, 95, 96
role in combustion, xix, 7, 8, 77, 90
chemical participation of, 9, 10, 13, 19, 22, 25, 26, 28, 34,

74, 78, 90, 95-104, 149, 150-151, 165-169, 174, 189, 192-193, 194
fixed air, Hales's, 9, 17, 18, 25-29, 32, 33, 90, 91, 96, 103, 145, 149, 154, 191, 193, 194
in minerals, 9, 23-24, 90, 95, 103, 104, 149, 150, 151
inflammable, 11, 24
"fixed air," Black's (carbon dioxide), 11, 13-15, 18, 35, 45, 47-49, 54-58, 67, 69-74, 96, 101, 110, 166, 193
as cement, 16, 33
Demachy on, 17, 18
as an element, 20, 33-34, 94
as an instrument, 20-21, 26, 32
as menstruum or solvent, 21
chemically inert, 22, 26
Boerhaave on, 26-27
Rouelle on, 32-33
mephitic, 52
in effervescences, 90, 91, 95
elasticity of, 168-169
Alkali, manufacture of, 46
American Philosophical Society, 40
Antimony, calcination of, 114-116, 119, 122, 124, 133, 134, 186
Antiphlogistic theory, 1
Arsenic, calcination of, 133
Attraction, doctrine of, 129
Augmentation of the calx, 5, 105, 111-124, 127-142, 144, 145, 148-151, 189, 194
Aveiro, 36

Bacon, Francis, 109
Baron, Théodore, 122, 123
Basalt, 165
Baumé, Antoine, 28, 94, 122, 126, 138, 164, 188
Chymie expérimentale et raisonnée, 138-139
Manuel de chimie, 126
Bayen, Pierre, 35, 71, 73

233